NEWTON RIGG COLLEGE
PENRITH

Christmas Tree Pests

by Clive Carter
and Tim Winter

ACKNOWLEDGEMENTS

The authors thank Alan Jones and Christopher Hood of Yattendon Estates and Tony Richardson of the British Christmas Tree Growers' Association for their help and interest in the development of this publication. Colin Palmer made valuable comments on the manuscript for us. Our colleagues John Williams and George Gate contributed to the high quality of the illustrations and photographs that have been used. In addition, we are also indebted to Øystein Austarå, Norway (Plate 11); Andrea Binazzi and Marco Covassi, Italy (Plate 56); György Csóka, Hungary (Plates 26, 27); Keith Day, Northern Ireland (Plate 37); Susanne Harding, Denmark (Plates 7, 8, 12, 21); Jón Gunner Ottosson, Iceland (Plate 17) ; and Mikael Münster-Swensen, Denmark (Plates 28, 29) for the use of their photographs. We also thank the typists, especially Pam Wright, for their help and patience in preparing the manuscript through various stages of its development.

ISBN 0 11 710339 X

Front cover, main image: Conifer spinning mite damage on Norway spruce (see Plate 62 in main text).

Front cover, top left: Female giant fir aphid (see Plate 10 in main text).

Front cover, second image on the left: Conifer spinning mite on the base of a spruce needle (see Plate 65 in main text).

Front cover, third image on the left: Spruce shoot aphid on a new spruce shoot (see Plate 37 in main text).

Front cover, bottom left: Single egg of a fox-coloured sawfly laid within a needle (see Plate 48 in main text).

CONTENTS

LIST OF PLATES

LIST OF LIFE CYCLE FIGURES

INTRODUCTION

Many species of insects are known to feed on conifers in forest plantations. Under these semi-natural forest conditions, the cost of insecticidal control can seldom be justified. When conifers are grown for Christmas trees in lowland arable farmland areas under an intensive short-rotation system, it has sometimes been found difficult to produce good quality foliage without embarking on some kind of insect control. This is especially so in the drier or mild-winter districts in Britain. In such places, spruce, for example, is far removed from its natural ecosystem. Furthermore, when the use of wide-spectrum insecticides is accompanied by almost total weed control, there will be few opportunities remaining for any insect predators to exist. So there is always the possibility of such an intensive system running into difficulties. Apart from cultural practices, the species of tree may not be adaptable to the new environment and any insects or mites associated with these outplanted trees may be raised from the insignificant category to that of a pest.

We have now recognized that at least 31 species of aphids, moths, sawflies, beetles and mites are of concern to growers of Christmas trees in Europe. Of these, many are of common occurrence, others are presently of limited distribution, and some are also troublesome in North American Christmas tree production areas. It is almost impossible to prevent the immigration of insects over a period of time, although the trade must be alert to the risks of movement of infested material. New infestations have arisen where medium and long-range (intercontinental) spread has taken place by the movement of plant material. Many insects take advantage of plants under stressed conditions, such as when being planted out. It is important to minimize this risk by only using the healthiest insect-free seedlings when planting for Christmas tree production.

Apart from the pest problems on the traditional Norway spruce, we have included here for the first time illustrated accounts and life cycles of insects and mites that are causing some concern to the growers of various silver firs, Douglas firs, pines and cypresses since these trees may be better suited as Christmas trees in some districts depending on local soil type, climate or market demand.

DIRECTORY OF PEST SYMPTOMS AFFECTING CHRISTMAS TREES

USING THE DIRECTORY

This directory is designed to help the user decide quickly which pest is causing the symptoms observed affecting the crop. Entries are arranged by tree genus, alphabetically, and then by the part of the plant in the following order: foliage, buds, current shoots, woody stems/bark, and roots.

The likelihood of a particular pest causing the damage symptoms observed is shown by a '+' in the first three left-hand columns. The damage rating in the fourth column indicates the severity of the problem as follows:

1 = slight damage, usually no control required

2 = moderate damage, some economic loss may occur in certain circumstances, e.g. honeydew and sooty moulds due to the spruce shoot aphid (*Cinara pilicornis*) will devalue the crop if present on the foliage in the year of harvesting

3 = serious pests that will cause severe damage with a consequent devaluation, or even total loss, of part or all of the crop.

Page numbers then refer the user to a more detailed description which also includes advice on control. Sometimes a combination of symptoms can affect the same part of the plant but are caused by more than one pest, e.g. on *Abies* foliage the presence of honeydew or sooty moulds and distorted needles indicates either *Adelges nordmannianae* or *Mindarus abietinus* as the cause. Consideration of symptoms affecting other parts of the plant, in this case whether or not there is any wool on the stem, can then help to make a correct diagnosis.

KEY

* Pests not yet known to be established in the United Kingdom.

** Very rare in the United Kingdom.

† It is sometimes difficult to differentiate between *Hylobius* feeding damage and that caused by voles. Close examination with a lens may reveal incisor marks left by the latter on freshly damaged stems.

†† Unlikely, unless crop grown in, or close to, conifer plantation.

DAMAGE SYMPTOMS

	Very likely	Possible	Unlikely	Damage rating	See page
SILVER FIRS (ABIES) – FOLIAGE					
Honeydew and/or sooty moulds present					
Silver fir woolly aphid (*Adelges nordmannianae*)	+			3	21
Giant fir aphid (*Cinara confinis*)	+			2–3	16
Balsam twig aphid (*Mindarus abietinus*)		+		2	10
* Siberian fir woolly aphid (*Aphrastasia pectinatae*)		+		3	18
Discolourea needles					
Conifer spinning mite (*Oligonychus ununguis*)			+	3	71
(*?) Eriophyid rust mite (*Nalepella* sp.)	+			3	14
* Siberian fir woolly aphid (*Aphrastasia pectinatae*)		+		3	18
Distorted needles					
Silver fir woolly aphid (*Adelges nordmannianae*)	+			3	21
Balsam woolly aphid (*Adelges piceae*)			+	1	12
Balsam twig aphid (*Mindarus abietinus*)		+		2–3	10
Mined needles (pale colour and hollow)					
Silver fir needle miner (*Epinotia subsequana*)			+	2	20
Defoliation					
Balsam twig aphid (*Mindarus abietinus*)			+	2	10
* Siberian fir woolly aphid (*Aphrastasia pectinatae*)		+		3	18
SILVER FIRS (ABIES) – BUDS					
Failure to open					
Balsam woolly aphid (*Adelges piceae*)			+	1	12
SILVER FIRS (ABIES) – SHOOTS					
Stunted, distorted, and/or killed					
Silver fir woolly aphid (*Adelges nordmannianae*)		+		3	21
Balsam woolly aphid (*Adelges piceae*)			+	1	12
* Siberian fir woolly aphid (*Aphrastasia pectinatae*)		–		3	18
Balsam twig aphid (*Mindarus abietinus*)			+	2	10

DAMAGE SYMPTOMS

	Very likely	Possible	Unlikely	Damage rating	See page
SILVER FIRS (ABIES) – STEMS AND BARK					
Sparse greyish wool present					
Silver fir woolly aphid (*Adelges nordmannianae*)		+		3	21
Whitish fluffy wool present					
Balsam woolly aphid (*Adelges piceae*)			+	1	12
Very large aphids on stem					
Giant fir aphid (*Cinara confinis*)	+			2–3	16
Patches of bark removed					
† Large pine weevil (*Hylobius abietis*)		††(+)	+	3	74
Patches of bark removed – smaller branches only					
Clay-coloured weevil (*Otiorhynchus singularis*)		+		1	70
SPRUCES (PICEA) – FOLIAGE					
Honeydew and/or sooty moulds present					
Green spruce aphid (*Elatobium abietinum*)	+			3	26
Spruce shoot aphid (*Cinara pilicornis*)	+			2	43
Spruce twig aphid (*Mindarus obliquus*)			+	3	44
Discoloured needles					
Green spruce aphid (*Elatobium abietinum*)	+			3	26
Conifer spinning mite (*Oligonychus ununguis*)	+			3	71
Spruce rust mite (*Nalepella haarlovi*)	+			3	41
Discoloured needles: seedlings and transplants					
Spruce root aphids (*Pachypappa* spp.)			+	1	40
Distorted needles					
Spruce twig aphid (*Mindarus obliquus*)			+	1	44
Mined needles (pale colour and hollow)					
†† Spruce bell moth (*Epinotia tedella*)			+	2	37
Notched needles (pieces bitten out)					
Clay-coloured weevil (*Otiorhynchus singularis*)			+	1	70

SPRUCES (PICEA) – FOLIAGE
Defoliation

	DAMAGE SYMPTOMS			Damage rating	See page
	Very likely	Possible	Unlikely		
Green spruce aphid (Elatobium abietinum)	+			3	26
Conifer spinning mite (Oligonychus ununguis)		+		3	71
Spruce rust mite (Nalepella haarlovi)		+		3	41
†† Spruce bell moth (Epinotia tedella)			+	2	37
Defoliation (leading shoots only)					
Gregarious spruce sawfly (Pristiphora abietina)		+		2	31

SPRUCES (PICEA) – SHOOTS
Distorted, swollen, pineapple-like gall

	Very likely	Possible	Unlikely	Damage rating	See page
Pineapple gall woolly aphid (Adelges abietis)	+			3	33
Large aphids present (spring and early summer)					
Spruce shoot aphid (Cinara pilicornis)	+			2	43
Sparsely foliated leaders					
Gregarious spruce sawfly (Pristiphora abietina)		+		2	31

SPRUCES (PICEA) – STEMS AND BARK
Patches of bark removed

	Very likely	Possible	Unlikely	Damage rating	See page
† Large pine weevil (Hylobius abietis)		††(+)	+	3	74
Patches of bark removed – smaller branches only					
Clay-coloured weevil (Otiorhynchus singularis)		+	+	1	70
Resinous exudations					
** Spruce bark tortrix moth (Cydia pactolana)			+	3	36

SPRUCES (PICEA) – ROOTS
White flocculent wax on smallest roots (seedlings and transplants)

	Very likely	Possible	Unlikely	Damage rating	See page
Spruce root aphids (Pachypappa spp.)		+		1	40

PINES (PINUS) – FOLIAGE

	DAMAGE SYMPTOMS				
	Very likely	Possible	Unlikely	Damage rating	See page
Honeydew and/or sooty moulds					
Grey pine-needle aphid (Schizolachnus pineti)	+			2	50
* Woolly pine-needle aphid (Schizolachnus piniradiatae)	+			2	61
Spotted pine aphid (Eulachnus agilis)		+		2	60
Discoloured needles					
Grey pine-needle aphid (Schizolachnus pineti)	+			2	50
* Woolly pine-needle aphid (Schizolachnus piniradiatae)	+			2	61
European pine woolly aphid (Pineus pini)		+		3	48
Conifer spinning mite (Oligonychus ununguis)		+		3	71
Spotted pine aphid (Eulachnus agilis)		+		1–2	60
Notched needles (pieces bitten out)					
Clay-coloured weevil (Otiorhynchus singularis)			+	1	70
Defoliation – any age needles					
Pine sawflies (Diprion spp.)		+		2	52
Defoliation – not current year's needles					
Fox-coloured sawfly (Neodiprion sertifer)			+	3	52
Defoliation – previous year's needles					
Spotted pine aphid (Eulachnus agilis)		+		2	60

PINES (PINUS) – BUDS

Mined					
Pine shoot moth (Rhyacionia buoliana)	+			2	58

PINES (PINUS) – SHOOTS

Mined, woody current shoots (July onwards)					
Pine shoot beetle (Tomicus piniperda)		+		2	56

DAMAGE SYMPTOMS

	Very likely	Possible	Unlikely	Damage rating	See page
Bent, soft young shoots					
Pine shoot moth (*Rhyacionia buoliana*)	+			2	58
PINES (*PINUS*) – STEMS AND BARK					
White, waxy wool					
Pine woolly aphid (*Pineus pini*)	+			2	48
Patches of bark removed					
† Large pine weevil (*Hylobius abietis*)		††(+)	+	3	74
Patches of bark removed – smaller branches only					
Clay-coloured weevil (*Otiorhynchus singularis*)		+		1	70
DOUGLAS FIR (*PSEUDOTSUGA MENZIESII*) - FOLIAGE					
White wool on needles					
Douglas fir woolly aphid (*Adelges cooleyi*)	+			3	66
Honeydew and/or sooty moulds					
Douglas fir woolly aphid (*Adelges cooleyi*)	+			3	66
CYPRESSES (SEVERAL GENERA) – FOLIAGE					
Honeydew and/or sooty moulds					
Cypress aphid (*Cinara cupressi*)		+		3	64
Foliage discoloured/dead					
Cypress aphid (*Cinara cupressi*)		+		3	64
Shoot dieback					
Cypress aphid (*Cinara cupressi*)		+		3	64
MANY CONIFER SPECIES – FOLIAGE					
Foliage notched					
Clay-coloured weevil (*Otiorhynchus singularis*)			+	1	70
MANY CONIFER SPECIES – STEMS AND BARK					
Patches of bark removed					
Large pine weevil (*Hylobius abietis*)		††(+)	+	3	74
Patches of bark removed – smaller branches only					
Clay-coloured weevil (*Otiorhynchus singularis*)		+		1	70

SECTION 1

PESTS OF SILVER FIRS

Plate 1. A Nordmann fir plantation grown for Christmas trees. Silver firs that are grown without some overhead canopy cover are more likely to suffer from aphid problems.

BALSAM TWIG APHID *(Mindarus abietinus)*

Tree species known to be affected

This aphid has been recorded from many species of *Abies* (true firs); particularly *A. alba*, *A. amabilis*, *A. balsamea*, *A. cilicica*, *A. firma*, *A. fraseri*, *A. grandis*, *A. lasiocarpa* and *A. nordmanniana*. Instances of *Picea* being attacked are probably attributable to another species of *Mindarus;* see *Mindarus obliquus* p. 44.

Symptoms and consequences of attack

The feeding of this aphid on the new shoots of true firs (*Abies* species) causes the needles to curl. Twig distortion, needle fall and stunted growth can also occur; in severe cases the shoot tips can be killed. Although there is some partial straightening of spring-damaged needles later in the growing season, the amount of damage persisting can be sufficient to spoil the appearance and symmetry of a young tree. An attendant problem is the profusion of honeydew that is excreted by the aphids and falls

Plate 2. Needle distortion caused by balsam twig aphid.

on the lower foliage. This sticky deposit becomes covered by black saprophytic sooty mould fungi. All of these factors contribute towards degrading the quality of *Abies* species grown as Christmas trees or for decorative foliage production.

Recognition in the field

Small pale green aphids surrounded by an abundance of fluffy wax filaments and honeydew droplets in the soft newly-expanding shoots in early summer. The attacked needles on the new shoots become bent or curled upwards from the time the bud scales are shed.

Annual life cycle

The aphids first become noticeable as the bud scales are falling from the new shoots in spring, when small aphids will already be present amongst the needles. This generation of aphids has resulted from females that hatched from overwintering eggs just before bud-burst. Almost simultaneously adult winged and wingless aphids appear on the attached shoots in early summer. The winged aphids are able to fly off and settle on other *Abies*, to give birth to young that develop into males and egg-laying females. The females lay eggs at the bases of the needles and cover them with white waxy threads that make them rather difficult to detect. The eggs do not hatch until the following spring, so the insect exists in this stage for eight months.

Recorded distribution and circumstances where damage occurs

This aphid species has a circumpolar distribution occurring throughout Northern Europe (Britain, Scandinavia) to Asia. Its original distribution was Palaearctic but, since its introduction to

Plate 3. Distortion of needles on new shoots of silver fir caused by balsam twig aphid in early June.

North America, it is now widespread in the USA and Canada where frequent damage is caused on native *Abies* species grown as Christmas trees. In some districts it only appears sporadically, but in others repeated attacks have occurred over many years on the same trees. Trees of 1 m high or more have been noticeably attacked more heavily than smaller trees; open stands and plantations on slopes with sunny aspects appear to be more susceptible to heavy attacks.

Minimizing damage and insect control

The choice of a fertile site with shelter from strong early summer sunlight would favour vigorous tree growth and minimize the damage caused by this aphid. There are good indications that earlier flushing trees are more susceptible to attack and so the use of seed origins or species that are known to have later bud-burst may help to alleviate the intensity of attack by this aphid. Under normal circumstances annual prophylactic insecticidal treatments are not recommended as the deformed needles will straighten a little and be hidden by subsequent shoot growth or removed by shearing; in addition, natural enemies will give some control. If young *Abies* grown for Christmas trees develop regular annual attacks by *M. abietinus*, some chemical control of the insect may be considered necessary and should only be used to protect the trees over the last two growing seasons before they are sold. Carefully timed spray applications are essential to prevent aphid damage in the current year. Spraying should be carried out two weeks before bud-burst, otherwise the aphids will crawl under the bud scales and get in between the tender new needles. High volume spray applications to run-off, and thorough penetration of the foliage, are needed to bring about effective control. [Take note of current Pesticide Regulations – see p. 85.]

Balsam twig aphid
Mindarus abietinus

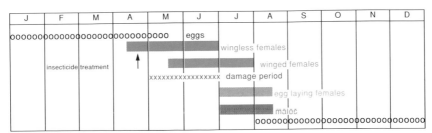

Fig. 1. Balsam twig aphid.

BALSAM WOOLLY APHID *(Adelges piceae)*

Tree species known to be affected

Abies alba, A. amabilis, A. balsamea, A. cephalonica, A. delavayi var. *faxoniana, A. delavayi* var. *forrestii, A. fraseri, A. grandis, A. lasiocarpa, A. nordmanniana, A. pindrow, A. procera* and *A. veitchii.*

Symptoms and consequences of attack

On young trees, foliage becomes distorted, buds fail to open and twigs become grossly enlarged, particularly at the nodes and around the buds; this is referred to as 'gout disease'. The shoot growth is distorted, often turning downwards at the ends. Sometimes the buds are partially enclosed in a knob of swollen tissue. The stems develop a marked taper after a few seasons of attack. Die-back of affected shoots follows and the symmetry of the tree is lost. The North American species of fir appear to suffer more than the European species.

Recognition in the field

The severe symptoms described above can result from just a few insects feeding on the twigs. The insects are partially concealed under bud scales, in crevices, scars or lenticels in the epidermis. This generation (the sistens) are only conspicuous when they become adult and secrete a covering of white wax-wool; similar generations follow which also occur on the twigs and stems until the autumn. The rarer spring forms (progrediens) are essentially needle-feeders and develop rapidly on the soft new growth.

Annual life cycle

The insect overwinters as an immature female sistens form and its growth and development commences during spring. These sistens become adult by the end of April and their eggs are laid in a cluster (average 150 per female) over several weeks next to where they are feeding. The newly hatched crawlers from these eggs are usually first seen when the buds are breaking and are very active for a few days only as they seek new feeding sites. They usually settle on irregularities in the bark where they insert their stylets. The crawlers from the first eggs that hatch are of the progrediens stage that feeds on the very young needles. This is usually a minor event in the life cycle of this adelgid in Britain, the reason being that eggs hatch before the buds have broken so most of

Balsam woolly aphid

Adelges piceae

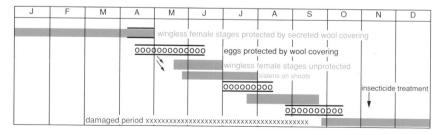

Fig. 2. Balsam woolly aphid.

this progrediens stage perish. If they do manage to find an available needle of the right condition they settle on the underside of the needle and lay a small clutch of eggs. The crawlers from these eggs settle on stems and twigs to become the next generation of adults. The more usual course of events for the bulk of the crawlers hatching from the first sistens generation that had overwintered is to settle on stems and twigs where they undergo a short period of aestivation (about one month). By July eggs are present again (20–40), and are laid in a cluster behind the adult sistens. Usually one further sistens generation occurs, reaching maturity by September, and the crawlers hatching from their eggs can occur up to October. These settle as before on the bark of twigs and stems where they overwinter. In warmer and more favourable sites the rate of growth, rate of oviposition, and duration of diapause may be significantly altered so that additional summer generations can occur.

Plate 4. Gouty growths on silver fir shoots.

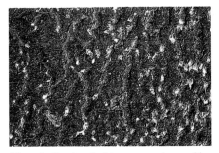

Plate 5. Specks of white wax-wool caused by balsam woolly aphid on the stem of silver fir.

Recorded distribution and circumstances where damage occurs

Adelges piceae is a native species in Europe, where it is thought to have originated in the south-east, although its precise origins are unclear, but now extends from the Alps to Norway and Sweden. In North America it has caused severe damage to the native firs in the maritime provinces of Canada and New Hampshire following an establishment early within this century. It has since spread throughout the *Abies* forests of North America to the West Coast. More recently it has been identified from material on introduced *A. nordmanniana* growing in Chile.

Plate 6. Severe damage to a silver fir *(Abies amabilis)* growing in a pinetum.

Minimizing damage and insect control

The balsam woolly aphid appears to thrive on exposed sites where soil moisture deficits are excessive. Attacks on older trees are of more frequent occurrence in eastern parts of Britain than in the west; there are several records of attacks near the sea coasts.

Growing *Abies* for Christmas tree production near to old *A. grandis* or *A. procera* is not advisable, especially under the climatic conditions mentioned above. *A. piceae* spreads by dispersal of the newly-hatched crawler stage after they climb to the outermost parts of the crown of the trees and are then blown away by air currents. The felling of heavily infested trees is best done in the winter months because during the growing season there may be crawler stages present at any time that could be shaken from the trees as they fall.

Insecticidal treatments against this insect, even on small trees, cannot guarantee eradication, nor prevent any insect damage. There are many natural enemies of the balsam woolly aphid in Europe and several have been introduced into North America to bring about control in the forest situation. Although this may regulate and minimize insect attack it would appear to be difficult to plan and manage on most of the small isolated plantations of fir that prevail. It would seem to be an easier option to grow those species of fir that do not react so obviously to this insect for Christmas trees and greenery production, possibly avoiding the planting of North American true firs for this purpose, with the exception of *A. procera*, especially in the risk areas.

FIR RUST MITE (*Nalepella* sp.)

Tree species known to be affected

Eriophyid mites of an unknown species were found in 1994 on *Abies nordmanniana* in Scotland. Damage to *Abies* due to eriophyid mites has also been reported from Denmark in recent years.

Symptoms and consequence of attack

In Denmark damage to *A. nordmanniana* is reported to cause a dark green to bronze discoloration of the older needles, which contrasts with the current year's foliage that is not affected. Severely damaged needles will drop, although this may be delayed until the autumn.

Recognition in the field

Damage by this mite causes a characteristic spotting of the needles only visible under high magnification. The spindle-shaped mites (0.1–0.2 mm) are slightly transparent, yellowish and difficult to see. The spherical eggs are similar in colour, 0.06–0.07 mm in diameter, and also found on the needles.

Annual life cycle

Very incompletely known. In Denmark seven to eight generations per year are recorded with adult mites active from about mid-May until September or October.

Recorded distribution and circumstances where damage occurs

In Britain eriophyid mite damage on *Abies* has been suspected several times but mites that may have caused the problem have been found only once. It is possible that this recent discovery in Scotland is connected to plants that originated from Denmark.

Minimizing damage and control

This eriophyid mite can cause serious needle damage which may be related to dry and warm conditions. Successful control can be achieved by using an acaricide such as dicofol + tetradifon, which is effective against both eggs and adult mites, applied as a high volume spray. In Denmark amitraz (Mitac 20) applied at 3 litres of product/ha in

600–1000 litres of water/ha has controlled the adults of this mite. Clofentezine (Apollo 50 SC) has been used against the eggs on *Abies*, but the Danish experience showed little extra benefit from applying this together with amitraz. [Take note of current Pesticide Regulations – see p. 85.]

Plate 8. Fir rust mite damage gives a dull appearance to the older needles of Nordmann fir.

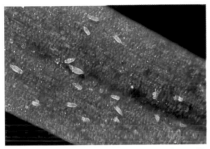

Plate 7. Fir rust mites on Nordmann fir needle.

Fir rust mite

Nalepella sp

J	F	M	A	M	J	J	A	S	O	N	D
adults											
?	?	?						?	?	?	
ooooooooo	ooooooooo	ooooooo	oooooooo	ooooooooo	oooooooo	ooooooooo	ooooooooo	ooooooooo	oooooooo	ooooooooo	oooooooo
eggs											
		◌								?	
	damage		xxxxxxxx	xxxxxxxx	xxxxxxxx	xxxxxxxx	xxxxxxxx	xxxxxxxx	xxxxxxxx		
			↑ ↑	↑	↑	↑	↑				
			control (as soon as damage is seen)								

Fig. 3. Fir rust mite.

GIANT FIR APHID (*Cinara confinis*)

Tree species known to be affected

Mostly recorded from true firs including *Abies alba*, *A. balsamea*, *A. bornmuellerana*, *A. cephalonica*, *A. cilicica*, *A. grandis*, *A. lasiocarpa*, *A. mariesii*, *A. nordmanniana*, *A. pindrow*, *A. procea*, *A. sachalinensis* and *A. sibirica*, but also on *Cedrus deodara* and *C. libani*.

Symptoms and consequences of attack

Dense colonies of the aphid on trees of all ages, producing much honeydew and giving rise to sooty mould deposits that blacken stems and foliage. These black deposits on the older foliage and stems persist for some months, lowering the quality of Christmas trees and making cut foliage for florists or Christmas greenery unsaleable. It has been suggested that very heavy attacks on the stem may be associated with leader damage and a fungal pathogen.

Recognition in the field

These aphids are very large, 4–8 mm long and have long dark legs. The wingless females are pear-shaped and of a dark brown or greenish black colour with a double row of blackish, slightly shining speckles and small flecks of wax powder in transverse rows on the upper surface.

Colonies occur on stems, usually on second year or older bark, and are frequently clustered around whorls and on the underside of branches. The species has sometimes been found on the larger roots of small trees.

Annual life cycle

Cinara confinis has been recorded in most months of the year but sometimes very large numbers build up and are especially noticeable in June and July. More recently, colonies on Christmas tree plantations have been reported during the winter months through to March, suggesting that, if conditions are favourable, colonies may persist over winter. Normally overwintering is in the egg stage; these are laid on the needles during the autumn. Occasionally this species has been found feeding on roots in the uplands, also on roots during hot summer weather, or enclosed in special earthen chambers constructed by ants. Winged females have been recorded mostly during June and July, when dispersal and colony collapse takes place, but they can also occur in winter or early spring, arising from the large dense colonies that sometimes overwinter. The egg-laying females that occur in the autumn are wingless whereas the males are winged.

Plate 9. Colony of giant fir aphid feeding through the thin bark of Nordmann fir in January.

Recorded distribution and circumstances where damage occurs

The species is widely distributed over much of Europe and south-eastwards to Pakistan and India, but is also recorded from California and eastern Canada. It occurs from the mountain tree line down to the lowlands. Exceptionally large colonies have been recorded from cedar trees in urban situations.

Minimizing damage and insect control

Incidents of *C. confinis* attacks have become more frequent since the recent increases in the planting of true firs for Christmas trees. It is quite possible that it could be introduced into Christmas tree plantations while in the egg stage on dormant planting stock. Female aphids arising from such eggs could be the start of colonies that would peak in numbers some months later. Similarly a single winged female, after a suitable period of flight, could also arrive in new areas from a considerable distance and initiate a colony in the same way. It may be necessary to control this aphid at any time to prevent sooty mould degradation of the trees. If large numbers are found infesting trees, particularly in the year of sale, they can be controlled with a contact or fumigant insecticide appropriate for aphids.

Plate 10. Giant fir aphid females are very large.

Giant fir aphid

Cinara confinis

J	F	M	A	M	J	J	A	S	O	N	D
few		many		wingless females				possible			
							?	?	?	?	
			few	many							
						winged females					
		xxxxxxxxxxxxxx		xxxxxxxxxxxxx		damage period					

Fig. 4. Giant fir aphid.

SIBERIAN FIR WOOLLY APHID
(Aphrastasia pectinatae)

Tree species known to be affected

Abies alba, *A. amabilis*, *A. balsamea*, *A. concolor*, *A. fraseri*, *A. grandis*, *A. koreana*, *A. lasiocarpa*, *A. lasiocarpa* var. *arizonica*, *A. nephrolepis*, *A. nordmanniana*, *A. procera*, *A. sachalinensis*, *A. sibirica* and *A. veitchii*. Of all the true firs, *A. lasiocarpa* seems to be the most susceptible. In the eastern part of its range this adelgid also makes small compact cone-like galls, principally on *Picea obovata* and also *P. abies*; these galls have not, however, been found on *Picea* in Norway although this insect is now well established there. Although not yet recorded in Britain, the description here is provided to alert Christmas tree growers to the very real possibility that this aphid could establish here.

Symptoms and consequences of attack

A heavy infestation of this needle-feeding adelgid causes the foliage to become badly discoloured, turn brown, and fall off, leading to shoot die-back. Prolonged attacks over several years have killed trees and also small stands of fir.

Recognition in the field

Yellow spots develop on the upper needle surface at the sites where adelgids have been feeding. On turning the foliage over to see the underside, some discrete white woolly tufts correspond with these yellow spots. The white tufts appear as curly, wavy threads and are secreted by the wingless adelgid underneath them.

Annual life cycle

In Norway, where the life cycle has recently been investigated, it appears that there is no involvement of a *Picea* sp. in the life cycle. *A. pectinatae* overwinters as immature females on the needles of *Abies*. By late spring they have become mature adults and deposit eggs within the woolly tufts. As the new shoots start to appear at bud-burst, the crawlers from the hatching eggs move immediately on to the soft new needles where they settle and feed. Some of these crawlers develop into winged females which disperse; others mature as wingless females, lay eggs and continue the wingless generations until late summer. The crawlers of the last generation hatching from eggs at this time settle and become fixed on the needles, but do not mature or acquire a complete wax-wool covering until the next spring. It is not known for certain whether the winged females are capable of reproducing viable offspring that will feed on *Abies*, since it is this specialized generation that initiates gall formation on *Picea*. The newly hatched active crawlers are more likely to be the principal stage that effects dispersal of this species. [Fig. 6 – see p. 23]

Recorded distribution and circumstances where damage occurs

Aphrastasia pectinatae is a Siberian species which has recently spread westwards to Eastern Europe (Poland, Latvia) and Scandinavia (Norway, Sweden, and Finland). It has not yet been found in Denmark or Great Britain.

Attacks have been particularly heavy on open-grown garden and amenity specimen trees in Norway and also on forest edges and plantations grown for decorative greenery.

Minimizing damage and insect control

It appears probable that this adelgid could be very easily introduced with dormant planting stock into new areas. Low density populations are not easy to detect and could increase rapidly and cause damage.

Local spread from infested tall old trees in the neighbourhood, or between trees within a plantation, can very easily occur with the highly active, newly hatched crawlers. These crawler stages, like those of other adelgids, are readily blown between trees on air currents.

In order to retain good quality *Abies* foliage it is essential to bring this pest species under control as soon as an attack is identified, otherwise needles will become deformed and hence devalued. The most effective time to apply an insecticide is in the late autumn when all the eggs have hatched and the only living stage is the newly settled crawler on the needle. At this time of year it is not enclosed by wax-wool.

Insecticide applications, where necessary, should be a high-volume spray applied to run-off; bearing in mind that use of a contact insecticide is necessary and the target is mostly on the underside of the needles. Gamma HCH and pyrethroids (cypermethrin and fenvalerate) have been found to be effective in preventing further insect damage to needles. Spray scorch from some insecticides can occur on very young needles especially during early spring when shoots are extending. An annual inspection in late summer, in case a control operation has to be arranged in the autumn, is therefore preferable to spring control which has the additional problem of the wax-wool covering over the adult female and her eggs. [Take note of current Pesticide Regulations – see p. 85.]

Plate 11. Overwintering stage of Siberian fir woolly aphid.

SILVER FIR NEEDLE MINER or FIR NEEDLE TORTRIX (*Epinotia subsequana*)

Tree species known to be affected

In continental Europe the host tree is *Abies alba*, but other exotic species of fir including *A. procera* and *A. grandis* are also affected. In Britain damage is most often reported on the latter species.

Symptoms and consequence of attack

Needles mined by larvae occur in groups and disfigure the foliage, often being located quite high in the crown on larger trees. Even low levels of damage will make branches unsaleable for decorative foliage. *E. subsequana* is not known, however, to cause similar economic damage to smaller trees in Christmas tree plantations.

Recognition in the field

Mined needles remain on the tree and appear brownish white or creamy. The larvae, which are found in the needles during June, are light grey–green to a yellowish green in colour with a dark head. Fully grown larvae are 6–7 mm long. Like all tortricid larvae they are very active and will wriggle backwards rapidly if the head is touched.

Annual life cycle

Adult moths fly in April and May when the females lay eggs in small groups on the uppersides of the basal halves of the needles. On hatching in June, the larvae mine the young needles which they penetrate via an oval hole in the basal half or towards the middle. At first they mine towards the needle tip, then to the base. Each larva will mine several needles before moving to the shoot tip where it feeds externally, but within the protection of a group of needles spun together with silk. When fully fed in July or early August the larvae drop to the ground and pupate in a cocoon spun amongst the leaf litter, where they remain until the following spring before emerging as adults.

Recorded distribution and circumstances where damage occurs

This insect is found in the southern half of England north to Herefordshire and Norfolk and is also recorded from Monmouthshire and in South Wales (Dyfed). It is also found in northern and

Silver fir needle miner
Epinotia subsequana

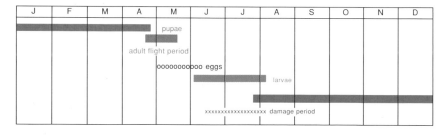

Fig. 5. Silver fir needle miner.

central Europe including Germany, Italy, the Balkan countries and in Russia.

Minimizing damage and insect control

No control measures are recommended. Careful inspections of *Abies* foliage in late summer are necessary before any contracts can be arranged for sales of decorative foliage.

Plate 12. Needles damaged by silver fir needle miner.

SILVER FIR WOOLLY APHID
(Adelges nordmannianae)

Tree species known to be affected

Abies alba, A. cilicica and *A. nordmanniana.*

Symptoms and consequences of attack

Needles of firs become distorted in early spring forming characteristic bottle-brush shoots. The new shoot extension is stunted and terminal buds fail to form. Withering and die-back of infested shoots follows.

Recognition in the field

The greyish black aphids can be found for most of the year on the stems and undersides of shoots. Individual insects have only a peripheral fringe of wax-wool around their bodies. When new shoots are extending, the new needles become infested with minute greyish green crawler stages. Galls are produced by a separate generation on *Picea orientalis*. The insects usually transform all the new growth from a single bud on a lateral shoot into a gall, each of which is spherical, 10–15 mm long, with much reduced needles, and are pink or red in colour but later darken to purplish brown.

Annual life cycle

The overwintering stage (sistens) hibernate at the needle bases and on adjoining small diameter shoots. They begin to develop again in the middle of March and, by the end of the month, become mature females that soon lay clusters of orange–brown eggs. Egg-hatch coincides with bud-burst and the emerging crawlers move on to this tender growth where they feed and rapidly develop into winged or wingless adult females. The winged females (sexuparae) fly away but are only able to accept *P. orientalis* as a host plant, where they give rise to microscopic male and female forms. These pair and lay eggs from which emerge the overwintering fundatrix generation, that can produce galls the next spring, although this is a relatively rare event. The wingless females (progrediens) that remain on the *Abies* foliage in the summer produce eggs that hatch into the sistens-generation crawlers that find resting sites on the needle bases to overwinter. The colonies can persist for many years on trees in this way, without the need to produce galls on *P. orientalis*. The young sistens crawlers are also capable of being wind-dispersed on to nearby trees. The period of greatest growth and reproductive activity in this species is while the new needles are still soft, pale green and also the most vulnerable. The galls formed by the fundatrix on *P. orientalis* mostly open in June to release the sub-adult gallicolae. These mature to the adult stage which is capable of starting up new colonies on *Abies*.

Recorded distribution and circumstances where damage occurs

Adelges nordmannianae is endemic in south-east Europe and is now widespread in Europe, North America and New Zealand. It appears to cause more damage to firs where it is non-endemic.

Plate 13. Shoot attack and die-back caused by silver fir woolly aphid.

Minimizing damage and insect control

This species, as is also the case with *Adelges piceae*, has been seen to be more troublesome when *Abies* is grown in open, very sunny situations where the trees are likely to be under more stress. Trees grown in dappled shade under the light cover of a deciduous overstorey appear to be less often attacked by this adelgid. Making new Christmas tree plantations in the vicinity of large old *Abies* species may result in many of the Christmas trees becoming infested. Old trees are seldom free of this insect and the crawlers can be easily distributed throughout the Christmas tree crop. For the same reason it would be unwise to raise *Abies* for Christmas trees in a nursery that has old *Abies* growing nearby.

As with other adelgids, any insecticidal control must be carefully timed and the application method must be extremely thorough (see under *Adelges abietis*, p. 33). Even so, control of heavily infested trees by high-volume appli-cation can be expensive and is unlikely to be completely satisfactory. By raising planting stock in nurseries well away from an infestation source and by being

Plate 14. Severe needle distortion on silver fir shoot caused by silver fir woolly aphid in early summer.

selective about a planting site that is without any stress factors, the Christmas tree grower can avoid or reduce the risk of losses caused by this insect. A number of insects do prey upon this adelgid, perhaps the most notable being various species of predatory beetles.

Silver fir woolly aphid
Adelges nordmannianae
and Siberian fir woolly aphid
Aphrastasia pectinatae

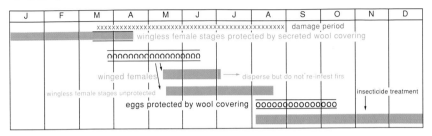

Fig. 6. Silver fir woolly aphid and Siberian fir woolly aphid.

PESTS OF SPRUCES

Plate 15. Sheared Norway spruce being grown for their larger size as Christmas trees for civic use. Special considerations need to be made to minimize pest damage if a good return on this medium term investment is to be realized.

GREEN SPRUCE APHID *(Elatobium abietinum)*

Tree species known to be affected

Most species in the genus *Picea* (spruces), see Table 1.

Symptoms and consequences of attack

Of all the insects that feed on spruce, it is the green spruce aphid (*Elatobium abietinum*) that can be the most devastating, especially when spruce is grown as Christmas trees. This insect is capable of causing total loss of mature needles at any time from autumn through to the next spring; serious damage is most often seen in late spring. After a severe attack, only foliage of the current year may be remaining by the end of the summer. This gives the appearance of a very gappy tree which is obviously inferior to an unattacked tree which can retain its dark green foliage for six or more years. In the year following a severe attack the new shoots often have much shorter needles, and the overall extension growth of the shoots is reduced. With small trees up to three years from planting it is not unusual for some of the terminal buds to fail to open following a complete defoliation. Other dormant buds at the nodes may then grow out as a result, causing the tree to have a poor shape.

Recovery from a severe defoliation by *Elatobium* is slow since it depends on new shoots masking the bare shoots resulting from the attack; a minimum of three years good shoot growth would be needed to enable such a tree to be reclassified as of good quality. The consequence of an attack one or two years before harvesting is very serious, as the recovery period of affected trees will mean additional years before they are saleable.

Recognition in the field

The first signs that aphids are present are most frequently seen in early spring, although they may also be seen as early as September when the trees are dormant. Individual needles here and there will be yellow or show a yellow band across them where the aphid has been feeding. The best way to see the aphid is to turn the shoot over and look at the underside of the yellowing needles or other needles nearby. Finding the aphids on Norway spruce and other spruce species with dark green needle undersides is difficult because the aphid is of a similar colour; on the blue spruce and those with silvery undersides recognition is simpler. Placing a sheet of plain white paper under the foliage and giving the suspect branch two sharp raps with a stick will usually dislodge some aphids if they are present.

During mid to late spring the symptoms of yellowing needles may be more abundant; many of those attacked earlier will have turned brown and be completely dead. The rate at which these needles fall away varies somewhat according to tree species and the season. If the lower foliage is seen to be glistening in bright sunshine during dry spring weather it suggests that a large number of aphids are present and some loss of needles will be inevitable.

The adult aphids are green, about 2 mm long, relatively short-legged and (by using a ×10 hand lens) can be seen to have dark red eyes. During May and June some of the aphids will be winged, but are never seen in any quantity because, when they have moulted to produce wings, they will take-off on a dispersal flight in warm bright weather. There is no host plant other than spruce in the life cycle of this aphid.

TABLE 1. GROUPING OF *PICEA* SPECIES ACCORDING TO THEIR SUSCEPTIBILITY TO THE GREEN SPRUCE APHID *ELATOBIUM ABIETINUM*

Group (susceptibility to attack)	*Picea* species	Origin	Needle retention	Foliage discoloration
1 least susceptible	breweriana omorika jezoensis polita glehnii koyamai smithiana rubens	N. America Yugoslavia Japan Japan Japan Japan Afghanistan N. America	Good (5–8 years)	None
2	orientalis schrenkiana brachytyla likiangensis wilsonii	Turkey C. Asia SW. China W. China China	Medium (3–5 years)	Usually none
3	mariana	N. America	Medium (3–5 years)	Slight (up to 25%)
4	engelmannii pungens pungens glauca mexicana	N. America N. America N. America Mexico	Poor (2–4 yrs)	Medium (up to 50%)
5	asperata x hurstii abies glauca	NW. China N. America Europe N. America	Poor (2–4 years)	Medium (up to 50%)
6 most susceptible	sitchensis	Alaska to California	Poor (2–4 years)	Severe (up to 75%)

SECTION **2**

Notes on the life cycle

Elatobium can be regarded from a practical point of view to be exclusively anholocylic in Britain; only rarely have the overwintering eggs been found. In other parts of Europe that experience a much harsher winter climate of long periods with air temperatures below -8°C, the aphid has to survive the winter in the egg stage. In Britain, the stages that concern us most are wingless parthenogenetic viviparous females and similar winged females. Although both these adult forms give birth to young females, it is the wingless generations that eventually cause most damage, since they can take advantage by feeding and breeding during the winter and spring. The extremely mild winters in the past have been notable for the severe damage caused by this aphid. By late winter *Elatobium* can be quite numerous and reproductively active, so that the spring months show a rapid population increase reaching a peak in May, and in lowland Britain abruptly ceasing during the first half of June. It is at this time that predation by other insects becomes apparent and, combined with the dispersal of the winged generation, aphids become scarce or absent by the end of June.

The use of suction traps that collect flying insects by filtering air has shown that winged migrants have a regular flight period in May and June. These traps detect the annual dispersal even at some distance from spruce growing districts. Their arrival on a Christmas tree crop, however, is extremely difficult to detect; furthermore it is not for another two months or more that the first signs of their presence and breeding can readily be found.

Risk areas and control

Low winter temperatures (below -8°C) severe enough to kill off the adult aphids and their nymphs on the foliage will prevent the build-up of aphid numbers during the winter months that could lead to severe spring defoliation. There is, of course, no sure way of forecasting if such an event may occur, but coastal areas with very mild oceanic winter climates could, for example, expect spring attacks more often.

In cooler parts of northern Britain and in the uplands, large numbers of active aphid colonies often cause serious defoliation in late autumn and early winter. The build-up of autumn populations has probably been linked to occasions where a short growing season has terminated shoot growth, perhaps by drought, and put the plant in a favourable nutritional condition to support rapid aphid growth and reproduction in the warm weather before the onset of winter. Early winter attacks are therefore likely to be more frequent in areas prone to large soil moisture deficits in late summer.

Growing 'quality trees' in these areas is likely to be more expensive than elsewhere in reducing damage by this aphid. When regular trouble is experienced, spraying with an insecticide is best carried out in August or early September. This is after the migration period and will give protection until the next immigration of winged aphids in late spring. *Elatobium* is not a difficult insect to control with insecticides that have either a contact or fumigant knock-down action provided that it is carried out in appropriate spray conditions and good coverage is achieved. The use of systemic insecticides is not recommended as they are not readily translocated in conifers. [Take note of current Pesticide Regulations – see p. 85.]

Plate 16. Green spruce aphid in its feeding position on a spruce needle.

Plate 18. Browning of old needles on Norway spruce in June caused by the feeding of green spruce aphid.

Plate 17. Green spruce aphid and needle discoloration.

Plate 19. Loss of all old and some current year needles caused by a heavy spring attack of green spruce aphid.

SECTION **2**

Green spruce aphid

Elatobium abietinum

Lowland Britain

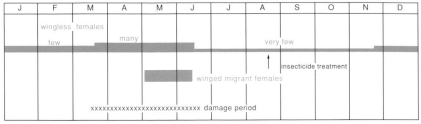

Upland and Northern Britain

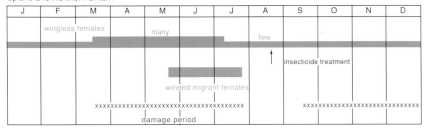

Fig. 7. Green spruce aphid.

An alternative approach to avoid defoliation problems from *Elatobium* is to grow a less susceptible species of spruce. Generally, the North American species are much more susceptible to damage than certain other species of spruce, especially those that are indigenous to Asia. Recent studies have shown that although *Elatobium* can feed and breed on all species of spruce, its rate of growth, colony development and subsequent foliage reaction can be quite different. Consideration should be given to exploiting these natural features by growing other species so as to lessen this insect's impact on Christmas tree production. Table 1, based on field trials and laboratory tests, lists species ranked according to their susceptibility to *Elatobium*.

GREGARIOUS SPRUCE SAWFLY
(*Pristiphora abietina*)

Tree species known to be affected

Picea species, especially *P. abies*.

Symptoms and consequence of attack

Bare or sparsely foliated leading shoots. Larvae feed on needles at the extremity of the leader and other dominant shoots in spring soon after flushing. Such damage occurs very quickly during May and June, the insects responsible often having moved away before the problem is noticed.

Recognition in the field

The immature stages are typical sawfly larvae (see under field recognition of pine sawflies, p. 52). The head and body are uniformly green, but with a slight yellowish cast, with distinct pale body hairs. Small larvae are difficult to see due to their cryptic coloration. The larvae are gregarious, feeding in a group together, and reach a length of 15 mm when mature. They take up an S-shaped posture when threatened, often also extruding liquid from their mouths.

Annual life cycle

Larvae feed on the current year's needles in late May and June. They pupate in oval brown cocoons about 6 mm long in the soil or under moss when this is present. The adult sawflies emerge in late April or early May of the following year. In May the females lay eggs into needles inside the unopened or expanding buds by inserting the ovipositor between the bud scales. Only a single egg is laid in each needle although usually from three to six eggs, and sometimes as many as twenty, are laid per bud. The eggs hatch in about 9–10 days as the bud flushes.

Recorded distribution and circumstances where damage occurs

Pristiphora abietina occurs throughout Britain and also in central and northern Europe, wherever *Picea* is found, but is absent from the Mediterranean region. Damage is more likely to occur in Christmas tree plantations that are adjacent to stands of larger spruce trees.

Minimizing damage and insect control

Damage is rarely extensive but is not usually noticed until after the larvae have left. If, however, larvae are seen at an early stage they can be controlled easily by spraying with a suitable contact insecticide. The use of diflubenzuron is recommended if the larvae are still very small when the spray is applied. [Take note of current Pesticide Regulations – see p. 85.]

Plate 20. Typical appearance in July of a shoot in the top whorl following attack by the gregarious spruce sawfly.

SECTION **2**

Plate 21. Damage caused by gregarious spruce sawfly showing dead and dying needles severed by the feeding larvae.

Plate 22. Larva of gregarious spruce sawfly.

Gregarious spruce sawfly
Pristiphora abietina

J	F	M	A	M	J	J	A	S	O	N	D
▬	▬	▬	▬ cocoons								
			▬ adult flight period								
			000000000 eggs								
				▬ larvae							
			insecticide treatment ↑								
				▬▬▬▬▬▬▬						
			damage period xxxxxxxxxxxxxxx								

Fig. 8. Gregarious spruce sawfly.

PINEAPPLE GALL WOOLLY APHID *(Adelges abietis)* or EASTERN SPRUCE GALL APHID North America

Tree species known to be affected

This is the most frequent and troublesome gall-making insect on spruce. Norway spruce (*Picea abies*) is particularly prone to attacks in Christmas tree plantations. *Picea glauca*, *P. jezoensis*, *P. koyamai* and *P. sitchensis* are often attacked quite heavily, whereas *P. breweriana*, *P. omorika* and *P. smithiana* are seldom seen to have any galls.

Symptoms and consequences of attack

Galled shoots develop into a pineapple-shaped structure. When formed on the lower less vigorous shoots, they tend to terminate growth, whilst the upper more vigorous shoots tend to grow beyond the galled area but at an angle from normal growth, therefore distorting the form and symmetry of the tree. At the end of the summer, the galls turn brown and dry resembling cones, and the associated needles die. The combination of distorted shoots, brown galls and dead needles results in permanently poor quality Christmas trees that may be unsaleable.

Recognition in the field

This tiny insect is difficult to see, and a hand lens (×10) is needed to locate the white woolly specks on the stems near to developing buds in the spring. Bright green pineapple-shaped galls, sometimes with deep pink edges in the summer, can develop on any new shoot. Similar brown galls, often in clusters, can be found at the base of adjacent shoots; these dead galls persist for many years.

Annual life cycle

The immature insects spend the winter with their thread-like mouth parts embedded in the stem tissue near the buds. At this stage, they are minute greyish black specks. As the adjacent bud begins to swell with sap flow in spring, so the insect commences its development. Before the bud scales fall away, the aphid (the fundatrix stage) will have reached maturity and laid a large mass of eggs all underneath a white woolly mass near the buds. The eggs hatch quickly in warm weather and the minute aphids crawl in between the soft new needles. By this time the overwintering female has already 'conditioned' the shoot by its injections of saliva during feeding. The minute aphids feed at the base of the new needles, causing them to swell and enclose the aphids within chambers. Several aphids develop in each chamber, and there are often 60–80 chambers to each gall. By late August the galls turn a purplish brown, releasing the sub-adult aphids. These crawl on to nearby needles and moult into winged females (gallicolae). *A. abietis* winged stages do not disperse significantly and move only a short distance to nearby trees. The individual gallicolae settle on the new needles of nearby shoots and each soon deposits a small quantity of eggs under the cover of its wings. On hatching, the nymphs crawl to the vicinity of a bud on a new shoot and insert their thread-like mouthparts into the stem tissue and remain there for the winter. There are therefore just two stages to the life cycle of this species.

SECTION **2**

Recorded distribution and circumstances where damage occurs

Adelges abietis is distributed widely in Europe and also recorded in North America where it has possibly been introduced. Damage is of greater concern to Christmas tree growers than to foresters. Trees of the most popular small sizes for marketing are most noticeably damaged. When trees are grown in open plantations, the more vigorous shoots often support much larger galls than is the case of older trees.

Minimizing damage and insect control

Nursery raised transplants may have the minute overwintering stages on them and therefore be the source of infestation in newly planted areas. Spread of this insect species in a plantation may be somewhat limited by the apparent reluctance of the winged gallicolae to fly. Consequently, individual trees may become heavily galled and also be a potential source of infestation to nearby trees. For this reason it is not advisable to replant in the gaps that are left in a plantation where trees have been lifted for sale. Some individual trees of *P. abies* do not appear to become galled and so resistance to the aphid has been suggested. The way in which such a resistance mechanism operates between spruce and this woolly aphid has not yet been demonstrated.

It is possible to remove the green galls by handpicking from small trees during early summer so as to make the trees saleable by the end of the growing season, but this is not practical on a large scale. Shaping trees by shearing or pruning current year's shoots in the summer is unlikely to reduce galling to any marked degree because the galls are formed at the base of the new shoots and will not be cut off.

Various insecticidal treatments that have been tested in recent years have met with mixed success. Spring applications of contact insecticides to kill off the mature fundatrix and prevent gall formation were found to be unreliable and too late to prevent gall damage. The egg clusters in April and May are covered with a water repellant waxy wool and are difficult to penetrate with sprays. Some success has been shown with soil-applied systemic insecticides to kill the aphids. The disadvantages are that such chemicals are often extremely toxic and there may be a need for total weed control or vegetation removal to enable good penetration of the chemical into the soil so that it is taken up by the tree. Furthermore, systemic insecticides are not translocated very well in woody coniferous plants for reasons which are not fully understood. Ultra low volume, controlled droplet applications of contact insecticides are also unreliable as the insect at the most vulnerable stage is minute, inactive, more or less dormant and tucked in fissures in the twigs and buds. It is for this reason that high volume insecticidal spray applications, that saturate the whole foliage, give the most reliable control. The insecticide needs to be applied between early November and the first week in March (mid–February in southern England) in order to prevent galls from forming. The timing of this treatment is of paramount importance otherwise gall control will not be achieved.

Plate 23. Pineapple gall woolly aphid attack on Norway spruce.

Plate 24. Developing pineapple gall caused by woolly aphid. The position of the fundatrix during the winter would be at the base of the bud, where the gall is formed, and is now covered in white wax. At this stage the subsequent generation (the gallicolae) are enclosed totally within the gall.

Plate 25. Immature pineapple gall woolly aphids (the fundatrix stage) overwintering close to the terminal bud of Norway spruce.

Pineapple gall woolly aphid
Adelges abietis

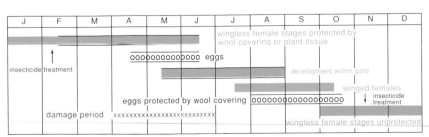

Fig. 9. Pineapple gall woolly aphid.

SPRUCE BARK TORTRIX MOTH
(*Cydia pactolana*)

Tree species known to be affected

Picea abies and *Larix*.

Symptoms and consequence of attack

Larvae tunnel into the bark on 5 to 15-year-old trees. If the larval galleries girdle a side branch this will be killed, rarely leading to death of the whole tree.

Recognition in the field

The presence of larvae tunnelling in the bark cambium is indicated by resinous exudations that form white streaks on the trunk. The yellowish or brownish frass (excreta) extruded by the larvae hangs down on silk tassels from the bark below where they are feeding. Larvae are small (6–7 mm) with a white body and a brown head. The adult moth is dark brown with whitish markings and a wing span of 13–14 mm and is rarely seen during the day.

Annual life cycle

The adult moths fly during June. They lay their eggs at night, in a bark fissure, usually at the base of a whorl. The eggs hatch in about 10 days and each larva tunnels into the bark where it constructs a gallery, lined with silk, in the cambium. The larvae are found in the bark from July until April of the following year when they pupate. Little feeding is done during the winter months from November to March. The pupae are found in a silk cocoon amongst the frass at the larval tunnel entrance in April and May.

Plate 26. Entry point of spruce bark tortrix moth at base of side shoot.

Plate 27. Bore dust (frass) and resin around spruce bark tortrix moth feeding gallery on Norway spruce.

Recorded distribution and circumstances where damage occurs

This species is rare in the British Isles, having been recorded in Berkshire and Hampshire only. In Europe it is more widespread and has been intercepted on imported Christmas trees.

Minimizing damage and insect control

Serious or widespread damage is extremely unlikely. However, if this insect is identified within a plantation, removal and destruction of the infected material will be the only option available.

Spruce bark tortrix moth
Cydia pactolana

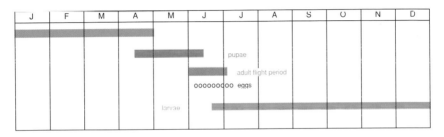

J	F	M	A	M	J	J	A	S	O	N	D
						pupae					
						adult flight period					
					ooooooooo eggs						
			larvae								

Fig. 10. Spruce bark tortrix moth.

SPRUCE BELL MOTH *(Epinotia tedella)*

Tree species known to be affected

Epinotia tedella occurs on *Picea abies* and probably most other *Picea* species. Larvae have also been recorded occasionally on *Pinus sylvestris*, *Abies* and *Pseudotsuga menziesii* in mixed forest stands but the species is not known to complete its development on these trees.

Symptoms and consequence of attack

Young larvae mine individual needles near the shoot tip, later moving to other positions along the shoot where they feed by grooving out the needle contents. Needles become yellow, translucent and are loosely drawn together and attached to the shoot with silk, thereby making a shelter for the larva and giving a very untidy appearance to affected branches. By spring, when the tree flushes, most damaged needles will have dropped, resulting in gappy patches in the previous year's foliage.

Small groups of mined needles occurring during spring and summer are due either to *Epinotia nanana* or *E. pygmaena*. Damage by these species is usually very localized and will not devalue the tree.

Recognition in the field

The larvae are greenish or yellowish brown with two longitudinal stripes that are pinkish brown to red. The head and a shiny plate of chitin on the next segment are brown. The larvae are 9 mm long when full grown and will wriggle backwards rapidly if the head is touched.

Annual life cycle

The larvae feed from August until late autumn. When fully fed they descend to the ground where they spin a silk cocoon in the surface litter, preferably amongst moss when this is growing on the forest floor. Overwintering takes place in these cocoons followed by pupation in April. A few larvae often remain in the spun debris on the tree during the winter. It is believed that these are diseased and will not pupate successfully.

The adult moths fly in late May or June. They can be disturbed easily during the day but are most active at dusk and during the night when eggs are laid on the host plant. Moths are brown and white with a wing span of 10–13 mm.

Recorded distribution and circumstances where damage occurs

This species is found throughout Britain wherever the host trees occur; also in northern and central Europe and the former Soviet Union.

Damage is most likely to occur where Christmas trees are grown in close proximity to more mature spruce plantations. Forestry Commission Research Division records indicate that it does not cause damage in Christmas tree crops grown in isolation.

Minimizing damage and insect control

Chemical control has not been used in Britain. Because of the difficulty of targeting the larvae that are protected by silk and within mined needles no recommendations can be made without carrying out efficacy trials. Diflubenzuron may be suitable if it can be applied to coincide with the eggs hatching. [Take note of current Pesticide Regulations – see p. 85.]

Plate 28. Adult of spruce bell moth.

Plate 29. Larvae of spruce bell moth.

Plate 30. Spruce bell moth damage to Norway spruce in January.

Plate 31. Frass and mined needles caused by spruce bell moth.

Spruce bell moth
Epinotia tedella

J	F	M	A	M	J	J	A	S	O	N	D
larvae overwintering in cocoons											
			pupae								
				adult flight period							
				ooooooooooooooooo eggs							
				feeding larvae							
						damage period xxxxxxxxxxxxxxxxx					

Fig. 11. Spruce bell moth.

SPRUCE ROOT APHIDS *(Pachypappa tremulae and P. vesicalis)*

Tree species known to be affected.
On the roots of *Picea abies*, *P. sitchensis* and *P. glauca*.

Symptoms and consequences of attack
Seedlings, transplants and small container-grown plants show yellowing on the tips of the foliage. Severe infestations in first year seedbeds are reported to be responsible for losses. The aphids feeding on the roots are thought to influence water and nutrient uptake.

Recognition in the field
White flocculent wax, secreted by the aphids, occurs on the smallest roots. The aphids are white or yellowish white and feed in small groups in amongst the wax they produce. Container-grown plants can be checked for the presence of these aphids by gently removing the plant from the container and examining the surface roots for the presence of white wax.

Annual life cycle
These aphid species can be found in the wingless stage throughout the year on the roots of spruce where exclusively female viviparous forms reproduce by parthenogenesis. Winged female forms are also produced on the roots in the autumn, and these migrate to either *Populus tremula* (in the case of *Pachypappa tremulae*) or to *Populus canescens* (in the case of *P. vesicalis*). These winged migrant aphids are sexuparae, which, on arrival on the fissured stem-bark of a suitable poplar, give birth to both small males and females. Each pairing results in a single egg that is laid in a bark fissure by the female. In the spring the eggs hatch and each nymph develops into a large spherical aphid causing the tender new leaves to become distorted, forming a leaf 'nest' that encloses a large number of offspring. These grow and develop into winged migrant aphids that are capable of infesting the root systems of spruce.

Recorded distribution and circumstances where damage occurs
Northern and Central Europe. Instances of spruce root aphids on nursery stock in North America probably relate to *P. rosettei* or *P. sacculi* (both indigenous to North America) and not to these European species. *P. tremulae* is found frequently in nurseries on container-grown seedlings and especially so when the seedlings become pot-bound. Trees growing in peat, or in badly drained soils, where much of the fine root system is near the surface, are more prone to attack.

Minimizing damage and insect control
These root aphids can infest planting stock very easily. Container-grown plants that are pot-bound or held over for two seasons with roots growing through the base of the containers are likely to become infested. If infestations are encountered in seedbeds or transplant lines for bare-rooted plant production, it would be preferable to use the land for non-*Picea* species the following season, since the aphids can survive in the soil for many weeks in the winter.

Plate 33. Spruce root aphid wingless stage.

Plate 32. Wax secreted by spruce root aphid on container-grown plants.

SPRUCE RUST MITE or ERIOPHYID NEEDLE MITE
(Nalepella haarlovi)

Tree species known to be affected

Picea: so far only found on *P. abies* and *P. sitchensis* but other spruces are probably susceptible.

Symptoms and consequences of attack

On *P. abies* affected foliage appears greyish at first but then turns reddish brown. Damage begins in the centre of the tree and then spreads outwards, leading in the most severe cases to defoliation of the older needles.

Recognition in the field

If eriophyid mites are suspected of causing damage then very close examination is needed to confirm their presence. The use of a ×10 lens may reveal pale orange spherical eggs, about twice the diameter of the silver stomata, on the needles. The elongate mites are amber in colour, a little darker, carrot-shaped and two to three times the size of the eggs. They have two forward-pointing long setae (hairs) positioned halfway along the body. Immature rust mites are almost colourless or a pale pink in colour. However, all stages are very difficult to see in the field, even with a hand lens, and examination with a low power microscope may be necessary to confirm the diagnosis. Eriophyid mites do not produce silk; see p. 71 for differences from the conifer spinning mite *Oligonychus ununguis*.

Annual life cycle

Very incompletely known. In southern England *N. haarlovi* eggs have been found during the winter, and adult mites have been seen in December and March. The overwintering stage of most species of eriophyid mite is adult females. A closely related species on *Abies nordmanniana* in Denmark has seven to eight generations per year with adult mites active from about mid–May until September or October.

Recorded distribution and circumstances where damage occurs

In Britain *N. haarlovi* has only been recorded by the Forestry Commission from Hampshire, Surrey, Berkshire, Derbyshire and Perthshire. However, there is great potential for these very small mites, which are difficult to detect, to be moved on nursery transplants and become more widespread.

Minimizing damage and mite control

Nalepella haarlovi can cause serious needle damage which may be related to dry and warm conditions. Successful control can be achieved by using an acaricide such as dicofol + tetradifon, which is effective against both eggs and adult mites, applied as a high volume spray. In Denmark amitraz (Mitac 20) applied at 3 litres of product/ha in 600–1000 litres of water/ha has controlled the adults of an unidentified eriophyid mite on *A. nordmanniana*. Clofentezine (Apollo 50 SC) has been used against the eggs on *Abies* but the Danish experience showed little extra benefit from applying this together with amitraz. [Take note of current Pesticide Regulations – see p. 85.]

Plate 34. Adult spruce rust mite on Norway spruce needle.

Plate 35. Spruce rust mite damage.

Plate 36. Spruce rust mite eggs on Sitka spruce needle.

Spruce rust mite
Nalepella haarlovi

J	F	M	A	M	J	J	A	S	O	N	D
adults											
?	?	?							?	?	?
ooooooooooo	ooooooooo	ooooooooo	ooooooooo	ooooooooo	ooooooooo	ooooooooo	ooooooooo	ooooooooo	ooooooooo	ooooooooo	oooooooooo
eggs											
	larvae	?								?	
		damage	xxxxxxxxxxxxxxxxxxxxxxxxxxxxxxxxxxxxxxxxxxxxxxxxxxx								
		↑	↑	↑	↑	↑	↑				
			control (as soon as damage is seen)								

Fig. 12. Spruce rust mite.

SPRUCE SHOOT APHID *(Cinara pilicornis)*

Tree species known to be affected

Most of the species in the genus *Picea* have been recorded as hosts when grown in Britain, but this aphid particularly favours those species with green rather than glaucous foliage. It sometimes feeds on *Tsuga heterophylla*.

Symptoms and consequences and attack

Aphid colonies develop on the new shoots and, while the needles are still soft, produce great quantities of honeydew. In dry weather the sticky honeydew droplets fall and put a glaze on the foliage. Saprophytic sooty mould fungi grow on these sugary deposits, turning the foliage black. This blackening can persist for several months thus spoiling the appearance and quality of the tree. Some minor needle loss can occur where the aphid colonies existed.

Recognition in the field

Large pale brown or greyish aphids tucked between the needles on the underside of the new shoot growth. The presence of this aphid on the foliage is often indicated by foraging honeybees collecting the sugar-rich honeydew on the shoots.

Annual life cycle

This is a very early species that can form small colonies on twigs before budburst, sometimes as early as January or February. In the first part of the year these colonies are exclusively female that increase by vivipary. The peak numbers occur in these colonies during early summer (May and June) when the new shoot growth is still very soft. Winged female aphids appear within these shoot colonies, particularly when the needles mature in summer and the colony strength declines. These winged aphids are capable of flying some distance for colony dispersal, and their production depletes the numbers of aphids in the original colonies. Much smaller groups of *C. pilicornis* may be detected in late summer on the twigs of newly hardened shoots. Amongst these are small, dark-winged, male aphids and orange–brown egg-laying female aphids with a conspicuous white tip to the body. The eggs are an elongate kidney-shape and usually laid singly on the current-year needles and are a greyish colour, covered with fine wax.

Plate 38. Lower branches of spruce with sooty mould fungi growing on honeydew deposits from spruce shoot aphid colonies.

Recorded distribution and circumstances where damage occurs

Cinara pilicornis occurs widely over Great Britain and Western Europe. Records suggest that it has become more frequent in recent times. It is one of the first species of insects to be found on newly planted spruce. This species flourishes and causes most damage in hot, dry early summer weather.

Plate 37. Colony of spruce shoot aphid with honeydew droplets on a new spruce shoot in June.

Minimizing damage and insect control

The planting of spruce on sites prone to water stress seems to exacerbate this pest problem. Districts with less than 1000 mm annual rainfall are troubled by this aphid more frequently. It seems probable that the spread of *C. pilicornis* into new Christmas tree plantings has been accelerated by using trees already having eggs on them, as evidenced by trees being attacked early in their first growing season. If large numbers of *C. pilicornis* are present in late spring they can be controlled with an insecticide that has either a contact or fumigant knock-down action applied at high volume. [Take note of current Pesticide Regulations – see p. 85.]

Spruce shoot aphid
Cinara pilicornis

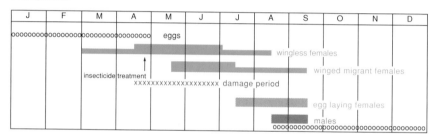

Fig. 13. Spruce shoot aphid.

SPRUCE TWIG APHID *(Mindarus obliquus)*

Tree species known to be affected

Those spruce species having blue–green or blue–grey foliage, notably *Picea engelmanni* and *P. glauca*, are most often attacked, but other species (*P. x lutzii* and *P. sitchensis*), which have the blueness of their foliage intensified when grown under the cover of protected cultivation, may also become attacked.

Symptoms and consequences of attack

When attack occurs on the tender young needles, there can be some needle distortion, but the shoot is not so seriously deformed as is the case with the related *M. abietinus* on *Abies*. Nevertheless, the aphid colonies do produce honeydew droplets when the shoots are in active growth in early spring. These honeydew deposits, sooty moulds and the secreted wax filaments contribute to a messy appearance that generally spoils the attractive foliage of blue spruces which this aphid appears to prefer.

Recognition in the field

White fluffy wax-like filaments, that are often stretched between the youngest new needles in early June, indicate the presence of colonies of *M. obliquus*. The aphids themselves are inconspicuous, small, and pale greenish white, feeding under the wax fluff that is secreted from their body surface. This aphid is not detectable before the bud scales have fallen from the extending shoots.

Annual life cycle

Mindarus obliquus has a very brief active period to its life cycle. It overwinters as an egg that hatches just before bud-burst, after which the offspring move readily on to the tender young needles to feed. If luxuriant plant growth condi-

Plate 39. Spruce twig aphid on new shoot growth.

tions continue, further generations may occur before a winged generation is produced. These winged females can fly to other spruces to produce males and females that pair and lay eggs. The life cycle is, therefore, adapted to a short season of plant growth, so it is in the resting egg stage for 10 months from July to May.

Recorded distribution and circumstances where damage occurs

This species has only been reported infrequently, but bad attacks have been seen at high elevation trial plots and with fast growing seedlings in favourable conditions.

Minimizing damage and insect control

Changes in the cultural practice when growing *Picea*, especially forcing the growth of spruce plants under protected glasshouse-like conditions, could bring this aphid into greater prominence.

Seedling plants could be introduced that have eggs on them which are extremely difficult to detect; and winged forms could spread this species also. If young trees of blue spruces are being grown for their high foliage quality, in conditions where this aphid is known, then some carefully timed control measures may be necessary.

SECTION **2**

SECTION 3

PESTS OF PINES

Plate 40 Sheared Scots pine being grown for Christmas trees. The difficulty in reaching every part of the foliage and bark with a contact pesticide at this stage can be appreciated.

EUROPEAN PINE WOOLLY APHID *(Pineus pini)*

Tree species known to be affected

Two-needled pine species but largely restricted to *Pinus sylvestris*; also known from *P. nigra*, *P. mugo*, and *P. contorta*.

Symptoms and consequences of attack

During a heavy attack, the needles of infested shoots become discoloured, turning pale greenish yellow (or sometimes even purple–brown), fall prematurely and result in stunted shoot growth. When really severe attacks take place during a dry growing season, especially on newly planted or small trees, some shoot death or failure to produce viable buds may follow.

Recognition in the field

Attacks are characterized by white woolly-wax specks between needle bases on the new shoots or along the bark of older branches. Continuous white woolly deposits can sometimes be seen along the whole length of the stem of Christmas trees, following the fissures in the thin bark. The individual specks of wax-wool are white and fluffy on the new shoots. Parting the wood should reveal minute (1 mm long) dark wingless adelgids, or immature females that are a reddish grey colour.

Closer checking of the wax-wool on the shoots during the growing season with a ×10 hand lens will usually reveal a tight mass of pinkish eggs. Later in the summer winged forms may be found settled on the needles. These hold their wings in a roof-like position over their abdomens and also produce white waxy wool covering a clutch of eggs.

Annual life cycle

The adelgid overwinters as an immature female on the stems, shoots or needle sheaths and reaches maturity in late March or April. Eggs and all stages of developing females occur from March through to early October. The most conspicuous period of activity comes after the first eggs have hatched, when the emerging crawlers move on to the tender green shoots and needles where they settle and feed. By late May these have developed into two distinct forms, either winged or wingless females. The winged females are without wax secretions at this stage and can often be found on the new needles from which they fly away when conditions are favourable. The wingless females, once settled, do not move but continue to feed and then reproduce on the shoots, producing two more overlapping female generations before the autumn. The winged generation is thought to be a vestige of a more complex life cycle (involving *Picea orientalis*) but this complete life cycle seldom has the opportunity to take place on account of the scarcity of *P. orientalis*. However, the complete life cycle is not essential for infestations to occur because the newly hatched crawlers, destined to be wingless females, are very active and are readily dispersed by wind currents. It is by this method that young trees are most likely to become infested.

Recorded distribution and circumstances where damage occurs

Pineus pini is found throughout Europe; other similar species occur in North America. Attacks and damage are often more severe in dry areas or in industrial or urban situations. Small trees that have restricted root growth (e.g. pot-bound in containers) or have had poor ground preparation prior to planting, also suffer more from attack by this adelgid.

Minimizing damage and insect control

This species presents difficulties when attempting control with insecticides because either feeding stages are hidden

European pine woolly aphid
Pineus pini

J	F	M	A	M	J	J	A	S	O	N	D

wingless females, unprotected when first hatched
as crawlers or during the winter
oooooooooooooooo eggs protected by wool covering
winged females
disperse but do not re-infest pine
oooooooooooooooo
Wingless female stages later protected by wool covering
insecticide treatment
oooooooooooooo
damage period xxxxxxxxxxxxxxxxxxxxxxxxxxxxxxxxxxxxx

Fig. 14. European pine woolly aphid.

or eggs are present. During the winter months the immature females may be hidden under the sheaths of the needle bases. From early April to early October eggs may be present which are coated with water-repellent wax and hidden by a mass of wax-wool. The only opportunity to effectively control this insect with insecticide sprays is in the autumn when the crawlers are hatching from the last batches of eggs and seeking places to feed and settle for the winter. At this time the various protective coatings on the insects have not developed.

The options for chemical control are either to use a contact insecticide, which must be applied at a high volume rate,

Plate 41. White wax-wool of the European pine woolly aphid on Scots pine stem.

Plate 42. European pine woolly aphid on Scots pine.

sprayed to run-off and preferably targeted at the crawler stage in the autumn, or to make two or three similar spray applications during the growing season.

Problems of effective spray penetration are likely to occur on older sheared trees that have dense foliage. Treatment with tractor-mounted lateral mist-blowing equipment is likely to be ineffective in penetrating to the stem because the trees further from the spray outlet are likely to be in the spray shadow and therefore only partially treated.

Predation by other insects is sometimes quite effective in reducing populations of *Pineus pini*. In particular, the larvae of flies in the genus *Leucopis* search out and feed on both adult and immature insects within the wax-wool. If predators are found to be present and allowed to develop it could obviate an otherwise expensive sequence of chemical control treatments. In taking advantage of natural biological control agents such as this it is advisable to consult a specialist entomologist for a correct identification and assessment of the situation.

GREY PINE-NEEDLE APHID *(Schizolachnus pineti)*

Tree species known to be affected

Mostly on *Pinus sylvestris* and *P. nigra* but sometimes on *P. contorta*, *P. muricata*, and *P. radiata*.

Symptoms and consequences of attack

This aphid can be a serious pest in Christmas tree production, where it feeds in dense colonies on the needles of pine causing yellowing of old needles and loss of vigour. The aphids excrete honeydew, which accumulates on nearby foliage and encourages the growth of sooty mould fungi and the accumulation of wind-borne debris such as dust and fluffy seeds of thistles and willowherb. Together, these factors can make the aphid-attacked trees unmarketable for Christmas trees. Heavily attacked small trees show a marked reduction in growth of shoots.

Recognition in the field

The presence of aphids can be detected by waxy grey masses on pine foliage. On closer examination these are seen to be composed of densely packed colonies of aphids; the various sized individuals being in rows along the needles. The abundant grey wax particles, produced by the aphids, surrounds them and to some extent the needles where they are feeding, thus disguising the individual shapes of the aphids.

Annual life cycle

The overwintering eggs are black in colour and deposited on the needles; in mild winters it can probably persist by parthenogenetic females. Eggs hatch in early spring, develop into wingless females which, in turn, give rise to further female generations through the summer months. As these colonies become overcrowded, winged females appear. Sometimes small trees become overwhelmed by the vast number of aphids, are unable to support their feeding demands, so the colonies rapidly decline to zero. During late autumn winged males and egg-laying females appear which pair and later lay the overwintering eggs on pine needles.

Recorded distribution and circumstances where damage occurs

Widespread and common in the British Isles, Scandinavia, and other parts of Europe, although the latter records probably relate in part to a closely related species *Schizolachnus obscurus*. In North America *S. pineti* appears to be well established in the western part of the USA where it is reported to be a pest on *Pinus sylvestris*. In North America Christmas trees are damaged by yet another closely related species, *Schizolachnus piniradiatae*. This aphid appears to have a very similar biology and is able to survive over a wide range of climatic zones (see woolly pine needle aphid).

Minimizing damage and insect control

Early control of this aphid, once recognized, is important since colony development is rapid and much of the foliage of small trees can be overwhelmed in six weeks. Cypermethrin or pirimicarb applied as a contact aphicide can give successful control. [Take note of current Pesticide Regulations – see p. 85.]

Plate 43. Colonies of grey pine needle aphid.

SECTION 3

Grey pine needle aphid
Schizolachnus pineti

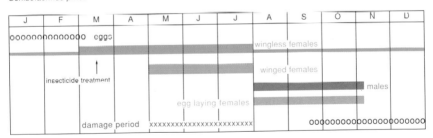

Fig. 15. Grey pine-needle aphid.

LARGE PINE SAWFLY *(Diprion pini)*

INTRODUCED PINE SAWFLY (North America) *(Diprion similis)*

EUROPEAN PINE or FOX-COLOURED SAWFLY *(Neodiprion sertifer)*

Tree species known to be affected

Most species in the genus *Pinus*; the most frequently recorded are *P. sylvestris* and *P. contorta*, also *P. nigra* var. *maritima*, *P. mugo*, and once *Pseudotsuga menzeisii* (larvae of *Diprion pini*).

Symptoms and consequence of damage

Defoliation: the needles are eaten away in patches often leaving bare shoots with needle bases.

Diprion pini is the species most often found on *P. sylvestris* grown as Christmas trees. It feeds on needles of all ages, chewing each needle from the tip, leaving the base as a ragged stub. *Neodiprion sertifer* only feeds on one year old and older needles. The rarely encountered *D. similis* feeds in the same way as *D. pini* on needles of all ages, the first generation preferring the previous year's needles, the second generation eating both current and older needles.

Recognition in the field

Sawfly larvae can be distinguished from those of moths by counting the number of pairs of legs, by the shape of the head and by their posture on the tree. Both kinds of insect larvae have three pairs of thoracic legs on the body segments immediately behind the head. The differences are that sawflies have five or six pairs of legs on the abdominal segments plus a pair of claspers on the last body segment, whereas moth larvae never have more than four pairs plus a pair of claspers, i.e. moth larvae always have at least two body segments with no legs behind the thoracic pairs. The head of a sawfly larva is almost round and often with very distinct 'eye' spots. Sawfly larvae tend to curl the head and tail segments back when threatened, taking up a C or S-shaped posture. They may also exude liquid from the mouth.

Larvae of *D. pini*, the commonest species, are pale yellow, shaded green and with a row of black dots along either side. The head is either brown or black and the mature larvae are up to 28 mm long. *N. sertifer* larvae are a dirty grey-green with a black head. This species has an almost continuous stripe along the side, the mature larvae being 22–25 mm long. The larvae of both sawfly species are gregarious, feeding in a group together. Larvae of *D. similis* are dark in colour with a double black dorsal stripe and white dots together with yellow dashes and comma-shaped markings along the sides. The head of *D. similis* is black and the full grown larvae, which feed singly, are up to 28 mm long.

Annual life cycle

Diprion pini usually has two generations per year with larvae feeding from late May to early July and again from August until early October. It is the larvae of the second generation (see Figure 16) that cause most damage to Christmas trees. *D. pini* normally overwinters as a cocoon in the soil, although cocoons of the summer generation are often on the tree among the needles. Sometimes cocoons of the

Plate 44. Large pine sawfly larvae feed in a cluster on both new and older needles.

first generation will not produce adults until the following year. Adult sawflies appear in May and again in July. The eggs are inserted into the edges of pine needles by the saw-like ovipositor of the females and are covered by a foam-like hard roofing.

The life cycle of *D. similis* is similar to *D. pini*, i.e. there are two generations per year. The overwintering stage is the cocoon which is spun on the host tree or adjacent plants. The larvae feed in June and again in September.

N. sertifer has only a single generation with the larvae feeding from May until early July. Cocoons are usually found in the soil, although a few occur on the foliage and may occasionally overwinter there before the adults emerge. However, most adult sawflies appear from the end of August until early

Plate 45. Larvae of fox-coloured sawfly feeding on older needles of Scots pine.

October in the same year as the generation from which they develop. The eggs are inserted into the needle edges in rows, which are sometimes interrupted, where they overwinter until the following May. Unlike *D. pini* the individual eggs are not covered by a foam cap.

Recorded distribution and circumstances where damage occurs

Diprion pini occurs throughout Britain, most parts of mainland Europe and in North Africa. *D. similis* has a similar distribution in Europe,

Plate 46. Larva of *Diprion similis* (the introduced pine sawfly [N. America]).

SECTION 3

except for the west of Norway where it is absent. In Britain, however, it only occurs in southern England. *D. similis* is also found in Turkey, Japan and Korea, and has been introduced to North America where it occurs in the USA from Maine to North Carolina and in the Central and Lake States; in Canada it is found in southern Ontario. *N. sertifer* is found throughout Britain although it is less common in the southeast. It is also found in Ireland and Europe, and has been introduced into eastern North America.

Minimizing damage and insect control

In Christmas tree plantations damage is usually localized and may only affect a few trees or even just individual branches. Hand-picking of larvae is a viable option in such cases, otherwise application of a suitable insecticide should be made as soon as larvae are seen. [Take note of current Pesticide Regulations – see p. 85.] In forestry conditions outbreaks will most often collapse due to a virus disease (especially in the case of *N. sertifer*) or by the action of naturally occurring parasitic wasps.

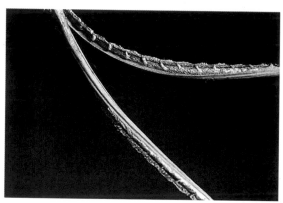

Plate 47. Egg scars of large pine sawfly.

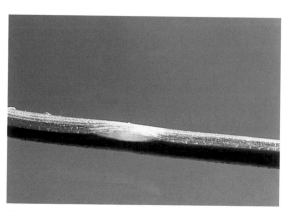

Plate 48. Single egg of fox-coloured sawfly laid within a needle.

Large pine sawfly
Diprion pini

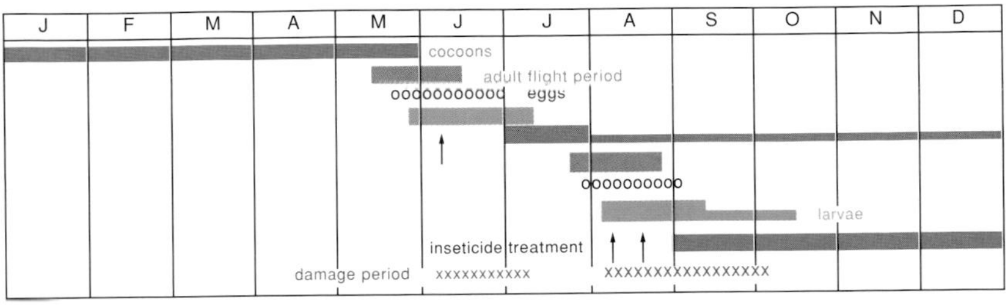

J F M A M J J A S O N D
cocoons
adult flight period
oooooooooooo eggs
oooooooooo
larvae
inseticide treatment
damage period xxxxxxxxxxx xxxxxxxxxxxxxxxxxx

Fig. 16. Large pine sawfly.

Introduced pine sawfly (North America)
Diprion similis

J F M A M J J A S O N D
cocoons
adult flight period
oooooooooooooooooooo
ooooooooooo eggs
larvae
insecticide treatment
damage period xxxxxxxxxx

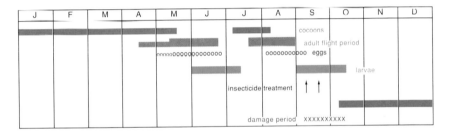

Fig. 17. Introduced pine sawfly (N. America).

Fox–coloured sawfly
Neodiprion sertifer

J F M A M J J A S O N D
ooooooooooooooooooooooooooooooooooooooooooooo eggs
larvae
insecticide treatment
cocoons
some overwinter
adult flight period
oooooooooooooooooooooooooooooooooooo
damage period xxxxxxxxxxxxxxxxxx

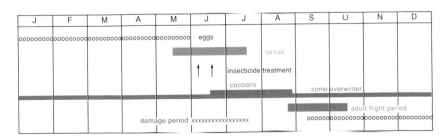

Fig. 18. Fox-coloured sawfly.

PINE SHOOT BEETLE *(Tomicus piniperda)*

Tree species known to be affected
Pinus, particularly *P. sylvestris* and *P. contorta*.

Symptoms and consequence of attack
The ends of the current year's shoots turn brown from mid-summer onwards. On Christmas trees such damage will be mainly towards the top of larger trees.

Recognition in the field
A hole 1.5–2.0 mm in diameter will be found bored into the shoot close to the junction of brown and green needles. On more resinous pines this will be marked by a ring of resin around the hole. If the dead shoot is split open a tunnel will be found extending up towards the apical bud and a small reddish brown or black beetle may be found inside this gallery. Sometimes several different beetles will have attacked the same shoot.

Annual life cycle
Tomicus piniperda is a bark beetle and breeds in recently felled, windblown or dead pines with a bark thickness of more than 2 mm. The female beetle bores into the bark and constructs a mother gallery up to several centimetres in length along the axis of the tree or log. Most mother galleries are bored in spring (March–May) but a few may be made later during June and July. Eggs are laid in niches either side of this gallery and the larvae each bore a tunnel at the junction between the bark and the sapwood. These radiate out, widening as the larvae grow, and culminate in an oval pupal chamber. Here the larva changes into a young adult beetle which emerges through the bark, leaving a scatter of emergence holes ('shot holes') about 1.5 mm in diameter. It is these beetles that cause the damage as they bore into the current shoots to feed and become mature. They overwinter either in a shoot or in a short tunnel made in the thick bark towards the base of a living tree.

Recorded distribution and circumstances where damage occurs
This bark beetle is found throughout Britain, Europe, and eastwards to Japan. It has been introduced accidentally to the eastern USA.

Minimizing damage and insect control
Damage will only be serious where suitable breeding material is close to the Christmas tree plantation.

T. piniperda may breed in stumps if these are left when trees are harvested. However, *T. piniperda* is capable of flying some considerable distance, certainly several kilometres, so sporadic damage may occur where there is no local source from which the beetles may have originated. There is no chemical control available to prevent shoot damage by this insect.

Plate 49. Shoot tips damaged by pine shoot beetle.

Plate 51. Adult pine shoot beetle boring in a current year's shoot.

Plate 50. Pine shoot beetle point of entry into a Corsican pine shoot.

Plate 52. Pine shoot beetle breeding gallery under bark.

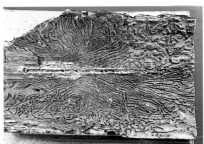

Pine shoot beetle
Tomicus piniperda

J	F	M	A	M	J	J	A	S	O	N	D
			many			few		adult beetles			
	oooooooooooooooooooooooooooooooo				ooooooooooooo		eggs				
							larvae				
							pupae				
					xxxxxxxxxxxxxxxxxxxxxxxxxxxxxxxxxxxxxxxxxxxxxxx shoot damage						

Fig. 19. Pine shoot beetle.

PINE SHOOT MOTH *(Rhyacionia buoliana)*

Tree species known to be affected

Most *Pinus* spp., especially *P. contorta* and *P. sylvestris*. Fast growing species such as *P. muricata* and *P. radiata* are particularly susceptible. Very resinous pine species such as *P. nigra* var. *maritima* are rarely attacked. There is also one record on *Picea breweriana*.

Symptoms and consequences of attack

Larvae of the pine shoot moth feed in lateral buds during the autumn. They overwinter in a hollow bud and in spring either bore into the leading bud or, if this has flushed, damage the stem causing the shoot to bend sideways. Such damaged shoots sometimes regain apical dominance causing a C-shaped bend or 'posthorn' deformity. Attacks are mainly on the uppermost parts of young trees.

Recognition in the field

The presence of a larva is advertised by a small resin-tent at the base of the attacked bud or shoot. This is constructed by the larva from resin and silk and, when new, will glisten in the sunshine.

Full grown larvae are about 12–14 mm long, dark reddish or purple–brown with a black head. The adult moths are silver with orange or ferruginous markings and a wing span of 16–24 mm. They are nocturnal but are often disturbed from the crop during the day when they will fly to another tree or flutter to the ground.

Annual life cycle

The adult moths fly during late June and July when the eggs are laid on needle sheaths close to the apical buds. When a larva first hatches in August it mines the base of a pair of needles before emerging and moving to a lateral bud. Here a protective resin-tent is constructed from silk and resin as the bud is mined (more than one bud may be attacked if they are very small). The larva then overwinters in this mined bud after sealing the entrance hole with silk. In March or early April the larva emerges and moves to a leading bud or shoot where a new resin-tent is constructed. The larva feeds in this new bud, or tunnels the new shoot if the tree has flushed, pupating in this last feeding place. Later in the summer, after moth emergence, empty pupal cases can be found protruding through the resin-tents.

Recorded distribution and circumstances where damage occurs

Rhyacionia buoliana is widespread throughout England, reaching the Scottish border on the western side. It is also in Wales and Dumfriesshire. European distribution extends to southern Norway, Sweden, and

Plate 53. Bent shoot caused by pine shoot moth larva feeding at base.

Plate 54. Pine shoot moth resin tent in spring.

Minimizing damage and insect control

Larvae can be controlled by two applications of a potent contact insecticide, such as fenitrothion, applied two weeks apart and timed to coincide with eggs hatching in August. [Take note of current Pesticide Regulations – see p. 85.]

Plate 55. Adult pine shoot moth.

SECTION 3

Finland; it is also present in Korea, Japan, and has been introduced into parts of North and South America. Damage can cause serious deformities in forest plantations. On Christmas trees shearing appears to keep damage to an acceptable level as the damaged buds/shoots are often removed.

Pine shoot moth
Rhyacionia buoliana

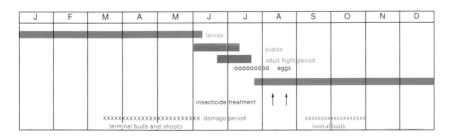

J	F	M	A	M	J	J	A	S	O	N	D
						larvae					
					pupae						
						adult flight period					
					oooooooooo eggs						
								eggs			
				insecticide treatment			↑ ↑				
		xxxxxxxxxxxxxxxxxxxxxxx damage period						xxxxxxxxxxxxxxxxx			
		terminal buds and shoots						lateral buds			

Fig. 20. Pine shoot moth.

SPOTTED PINE APHID *(Eulachnus agilis)*

Tree species known to be affected

Pinus sylvestris, P. nigra var. *maritima, P. halepensis, P. pinaster* and *P. strobus.*

Symptoms and consequences of attack

This foliage-feeding aphid causes premature drop of the previous year's needles, although it will also feed on the current-year's needles. It is frequently found on needles that are showing senescing symptoms. This aphid also shares the same needles as those occupied by the grey pine-needle aphid *(S. pineti)*. In both cases the needles are physiologically changed and appear to be of benefit to this species.

Recognition in the field

This aphid is small and bright green with pale legs. It has an elongate body, the surface of which is dotted with fine dark specks. Although its colour and shape blend well with pine foliage, it can be easily detected, for it is readily disturbed and becomes active by walking around when foliage is examined.

Annual life cycle

The overwintering eggs are usually laid singly in leaf scars on the shoots in the autumn. The female aphids that hatch from these eggs have a long life span of two or three months, but are slow to reach maturity before they give birth to 10–20 aphids. Winged and wingless females occur on the foliage from June to October. The population peaks in spring but then decreases to an extremely low level from late June to early August. The aphid numbers increase again in late summer until a peak is reached in the early autumn.

Recorded distribution and circumstances where damage occurs

Frequent in pine growing areas, particularly in the southern and eastern counties of Britain, but also from Scandinavia across Europe to Turkey, China, and parts of eastern North America. High temperatures considerably shorten the time taken for this species to reach maturity and can double the birth rate.

Minimizing damage and insect control

Healthy foliage and good needle retention make pines less attractive to this aphid. Oversized transplants and pot-bound container-grown plants are likely to be attacked. If insecticidal treatments are to be applied, they are probably most effective in mid-May, which is after the overwintering eggs have all hatched, but before the first generation has started to reproduce.

Plate 56. Needle discoloration caused by spotted pine aphid.

Spotted pine aphid
Eulachnus agilis

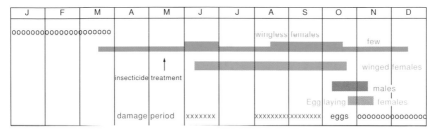

Fig. 21. Spotted pine aphid.

WOOLLY PINE-NEEDLE APHID
(Schizolachnus piniradiatae)

Tree species known to be affected

Pinus radiata, *P. ponderosa*, *P. ponderosa* var. *scopulorum*, *P. sabiniana*, *P. contorta* var. *murrayana*, *P. resinosa*, and *P. banksiana*.

Symptoms and consequences of attack

Similar to *Schizolachnus pineti*.

Recognition in the field

Aphids are dark green, long-legged, and covered with cottony wax. Colonies form a line along the needles all heading in one direction.

Annual life cycle

Essentially similar to *S. pineti*. The following details of the life cycle were originally recorded in Ontario, Canada. The eggs can hatch by early April. When the developing aphids are over 20 days old they become adult females and produce young viviparously congregating in rows along the needles where they feed until adult. They then disperse and start up their own colonies. Winged females occur from June to late August, which is the period when they are first noticed on previously uninfested trees.

Six or more generations can occur over the summer season until wingless egg-laying females and winged males are produced. The shiny black eggs are laid in clusters of four, end to end, along the needles.

Recorded distribution and circumstances where damage occurs

Canada (Nova Scotia to British Columbia) and New Mexico in western USA. Although not considered a forest pest, it is conceivable that it could be troublesome to Christmas tree growers on account of its close similarity with the grey pine-needle aphid *S. pineti*.

Minimizing damage and insect control

High mortality of overwintering eggs has been recorded in early spring. Parasitoids, predators, and an entomophagous fungal disease all appear to exert a strong regulating influence on the aphid numbers. So, although this aphid has a high theoretical pest potential, damaging populations have never been realized.

SECTION 4

PESTS OF OTHER CONIFERS

CYPRESS APHID *(Cinara cupressi)*

Tree species known to be affected

Mainly on species in the genus *Cupressus*, but also on *Cupressocyparis leylandii*, *Chamaecyparis lawsoniana* and *Thuja*.

Symptoms and consequences of attack

Damage to denser trimmed trees or hedges is usually first noticed in late May or early June when patches of foliage towards the base of the tree become yellowish or straw coloured. This discoloration may spread upwards and the colour change can occur within 7–10 days of initial infestation. Later the foliage turns brown and appears dried up, the lower branches often dying back. In extreme cases the damage can extend to the whole crown of the tree. Sooty moulds (saprophytic fungi) may grow on the sugar-rich honeydew excreted by the aphids, giving a blackened appearance to the stems and foliage where the aphid, colonies are, or have been, feeding in large numbers. This symptom is not obvious when only a few aphids are present. In the late summer, wasps foraging for sugar in the honeydew can draw attention to infestations of this aphid.

Recognition in the field

Cinara cupressi is a fairly large aphid, but it can be very difficult to find since small colonies closely resemble the colour and texture of small twigs amongst the foliage where they feed. Individuals range from 1.8 to 3.9 mm long and have an overall greyish appearance. On close examination, the body colour is greyish to yellowish brown beneath a hairy covering. They are pear-shaped and have two black stripes running about one-third of their length from the head.

Annual life cycle

The aphids, found from April to November, are mainly wingless parthenogenetic females which give birth to live young. From June to August winged females also occur; egg-laying females and males occur in the autumn. It seems possible that wingless parthenogenetic females may sometimes overwinter under mild conditions. This would give the aphid a good start to rapid build-up in a mild spring season.

Recorded distribution and circumstances where damage occurs

This species is widely distributed in the warmer parts of Europe where it is found mainly on *Cupressus* species. In Britain it has been known in south-west England for over a century and was associated with damage to *Cupressus macrocarpa*; subsequently high infestations have occurred in southern England. In 1987 this aphid was recorded on × *Cupressocyparis leylandii* in a few locations in England, but by 1988 it became far more widespread; although still occurring mainly in southern England it was also found from South Wales to Shropshire and Lincolnshire. The unprecedented increase in 1988 may have resulted from aphids overwintering successfully through the mild winter of 1987/88, or was perhaps caused by an immigration of this aphid from Europe.

Minimizing damage and insect control

Cinara cupressi needs to feed for only a short period of time to initiate foliar colour changes and eventual death of affected parts of the tree. Only the shoots on which the colonies are feeding become damaged. This rapid plant response means that any insecticidal treatment that is intended to prevent

Plate 57. Branch die-back on Leyland cypress caused by cypress aphid.

Plate 58. Colony of cypress aphids.

damage needs to be applied very soon after winged aphids arrive on the tree. However, as small colonies of this aphid are difficult to see, the whole of an affected plant needs to be treated with a suitable insecticide to prevent further damage to the crown or adjacent plants in hedges and windbreaks. Typically, damage symptoms continue to develop for a time after the aphids responsible have been killed. The reason why this happens has not been explained.

SECTION 4

Cypress aphid
Cinara cupressi

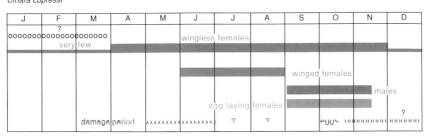

Fig. 22. Cypress aphid.

DOUGLAS FIR WOOLLY APHID *(Adelges cooleyi)* or COOLEY SPRUCE GALL APHID (North America)

Tree species known to be affected

On the foliage of *Pseudotsuga macrocarpa*, *P. menziesii*, and *P. menziesii* var. *glauca*. Galls may be formed on various North American spruces, *Picea engelmanni*, *P. glauca* and *P. pungens*, but especially on *P. sitchensis*.

Symptoms and consequences of attack

Heavy attacks by the insect (i.e. several adelgids on each needle) can cause a conspicuous reduction in vigour of nursery stock and in plantations during their early years of establishment. Needle drop occurs sometimes, but honeydew deposits from this species also add to the loss of foliage quality and therefore are very damaging to Christmas tree production.

On spruce this species induces galls that are characteristically very elongate and often twisted. These turn brown and dead in late summer, and remain on the trees, which can disrupt the symmetry of the whorls and branching pattern. A significant number of galls are sometimes produced on small trees, tending to deform them and stunt further shoot growth beyond the gall.

Recognition in the field

Adelges cooleyi produces conspicuous white wax-wool tufts along the undersides of the needles of *Pseudotsuga*, being especially noticeable in early spring. The most serious damage is caused by the insects feeding on the soft young needles, making them yellowish and permanently twisted. This damage commences as soon as the first spring generation settles amongst the needles when the bud scales begin to fall away.

Annual life cycle

The only overwintering stage of this insect on *Pseudotsuga* is the immature female that is fixed on the underside of the needles, usually along the white stomatal lines. Before bud-burst in May, these females have reached maturity and laid eggs under a blob of white wax-wool on the old needles. The crawlers hatching from these eggs settle and feed on the new needles. Some of the settled crawlers develop into winged females which disperse; others mature into parthenogenetic wingless females and lay eggs to reproduce the same stage. This occurs at least once until the end of summer but, for each generation, the hatching crawlers seek new sites to settle and feed on the needles. By late summer, only dark immature females are to be found on the needles. This is the overwintering stage that remains fixed to the same position until the following spring when the cycle on Douglas fir is repeated.

When the winged females settle on the various *Picea* species mentioned above, they also lay eggs from which males and females emerge. These pair and their resultant offspring settle near to a bud for the winter period. Early the following spring these develop rapidly into the fundatrix adult stage and become covered with a wax-wool mass under which eggs are laid. Egg-hatch coincides with bud-burst and the emerging crawlers feed at the base of the new needles which become swollen and grow together, thus enclosing the crawlers and forming a gall on a foreshortened shoot. These galls start to dry out from early August onwards, releasing the now larger, but immature, females. Within a few hours of release these moult into fully winged females and disperse. If these arrive on *Pseudotsuga* and settle on the needles they are capable of initiating a new cycle. Eggs are laid under the cover of their wings.

The hatching crawlers move to a feeding site on the new needles where they settle, turn black and become fixed over winter in this position in the same manner and having the same subsequent development as the offspring from the wingless females on *Pseudotsuga*.

Recorded distribution and circumstances where damage occurs

This species is native to western North America (known principally from *Pseudotsuga*) and was first recorded in Britain in 1913 when its attacks were only known to occur on *Pseudotsuga*. It was not until 1935 that the galls of *A. cooleyi* were found on Sitka spruce in Britain. It has since been found over much of the British Isles on both hosts, but especially in those districts where *Pseudotsuga* is commonly grown. Open grown trees on poor sites in low rainfall districts are more prone to heavy attack. The Colorado Douglas fir (*P. menziesii* var. *glauca*) has a visual appeal on account of its blue foliage but, although reputed to be much more resistant to *A. cooleyi* attacks, it is disadvantaged by its slower growth and also suffers badly from needle-cast diseases in Britain.

Minimizing damage and insect control

The insect is not easy to detect on small *Pseudotsuga* transplants in the dormant season, yet it is from this beginning that an infestation could develop.

In addition, local spread from infested tall old trees in the neighbourhood, or between trees within a plantation, can occur very easily through wind dispersal of the highly active, newly hatched crawlers.

In order to retain good quality foliage it is essential to bring this pest species under control as soon as an attack is identified, otherwise needles will become deformed and the tree devalued. The most effective time to apply an insecticide is in the late autumn when all the eggs have hatched and the only living stage is the newly settled crawler on the needle. At this time of year they are not enclosed by wax-wool, and in

Plate 59. Yellow needle flecking and distortion caused by Douglas fir woolly aphid.

SECTION 4

Britain they remain in this stage until the end of February.

Insecticide applications, where necessary, should be a high-volume spray applied to run-off, bearing in mind that use of a contact insecticide is necessary and the target is mostly on the underside of the needles. Gamma HCH and pirimicarb (although the latter is less effective at low temperatures) have been found to be effective in preventing further insect damage to needles. An annual inspection in late summer, in case a control operation has to be arranged for the autumn, is therefore preferable to a spring control, which has the additional problem of the wax-wool covering over the adult female and her eggs. [Take note of current Pesticide Regulations – see p. 85.]

Similar inspection and control dates would be appropriate to prevent gall formation on spruce shoots. Applications of insecticides in the early spring may be too late to prevent deformities caused by the overwintering fundatrix feeding near the buds at the end of the winter period.

Plate 60. White wax-wool tufts of Douglas fir woolly aphid.

Douglas fir woolly aphid
Adelges cooleyi

J	F	M	A	M	J	J	A	S	O	N	D

wingless female stages protected by secreted wool covering

oooooooooo

disperse to Sitka spruce (year 1)

winged females

return from spruce galls (year 2)

eggs protected by wool covering oooooooooooooooooooooo

wingless females, unprotected when first hatched as crawlers or during the winter

damage period xxxxxxxxxxxxxxxxxxxxxxx

insecticide treatment

Fig. 23. Douglas fir woolly aphid.

SECTION 5

GENERAL PESTS

CLAY-COLOURED WEEVIL
(Otiorhynchus singularis)

Tree species known to be affected

Damage has been recorded on a wide range of both conifers and broadleaved trees. The coniferous hosts include *Picea* (spruces), *Pinus* (pines), *Pseudotsuga menziesii* (Douglas fir), *Tsuga heterophylla* (western hemlock), *Thuja plicata* (western red cedar) as well as *Larix* (larches) and *Chamaecyparis lawsoniana* (Lawson cypress). The age of the host tree is a more important factor than species, since damage is usually recorded in the nursery or on transplants and young trees (see below).

Symptoms and consequence of attack

Adult weevils feed on the bark of the stems of young trees and also on the needles. Removal of quite large and irregular areas of bark can girdle the stem, effectively ring-barking it and causing the subsequent death of the shoot. Damage to needles consists of the removal of triangular notches; sometimes many of the needles on a leader of *Picea* can be damaged making it bare.

Recognition in the field

Adult weevils are 5–7 mm long, black but covered with greyish brown hairs; a colouring that suggests this beetle's common name. The weevils are pear-shaped with a short and broad snout, on the end of which are placed the characteristic elbowed antennae. The wing cases or elytra are fused together because *O. singularis* does not have functional wings. Adult beetles hide during the day in the soil or beneath vegetation on the ground but can be found feeding during late evening in the spring, by torchlight (in Scotland this is after 22.00 hours during late April and in May). The larvae are white grubs, up to 8 mm long, with a brown head. They live in the soil feeding on fine roots of herbs and trees but these larvae cause no significant damage to Christmas trees.

Annual life cycle

Adult weevils are active from April until October. Eggs are laid in the soil during the summer and take about five weeks to hatch. Larvae develop throughout the winter and pupate in early spring in the soil. Some larvae may take another year before pupating. Almost all *O. singularis* are females and breed parthogenetically, i.e. the eggs do not require fertilization to develop.

Recorded distribution and circumstances where damage occurs

This weevil is widely distributed in Britain and Western Europe, particularly in grassland areas. Damage is most likely to occur on newly cultivated land or where there is a good cover of grass and perennial weeds between the trees.

Plate 61. Clay-coloured weevil damage on Norway spruce.

Minimizing damage and insect control

Damage to Christmas trees by *O. singularis* in Britain is not very common. In the unlikely event that serious damage is noted, the adult weevils can be controlled by drenching affected trees with a suitable insecticide. In Scotland fenitrothion applied at seven day intervals gave effective control on raspberries, especially when applied after dark while the weevils were feeding. The use of gamma HCH or synthetic pyrethroids was less effective. [Take note of current Pesticide Regulations – see p. 85.]

Clay–coloured weevil
Otiorhynchus singularis

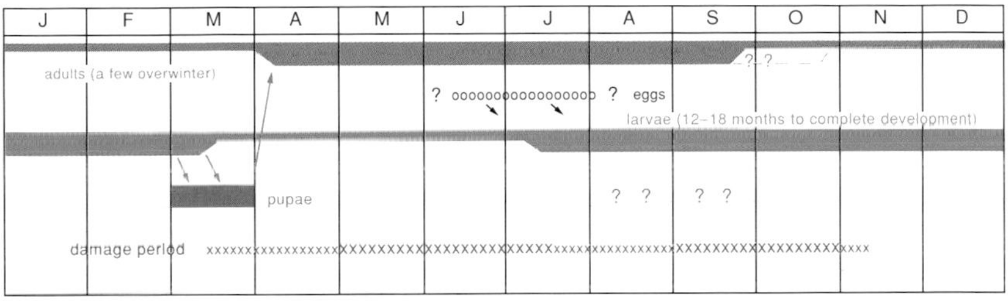

J	F	M	A	M	J	J	A	S	O	N	D
adults (a few overwinter)								? ?			
				? oooooooooooooooop ? eggs							
						larvae (12–18 months to complete development)					
		pupae				? ?	? ?				
damage period	xxxxxxxxxxxxxxxxxxxxxxxxxxxxxxxxxxxxxxxxxxxxxxxxxxxxxxxxxxxxxxxxxxxxxxxxxxxxxx										

Fig. 24. Clay-coloured weevil.

CONIFER SPINNING MITE
(Oligonychus ununguis)

Tree species known to be affected

This species has been recorded on a wide range of conifers in Britain, but on Christmas trees mainly damaging *Picea abies* and more rarely *Pinus sylvestris*.

Symptoms and consequence of attack

Damaged needles have a yellow speckled appearance at first, but later turn to a bronze colour. The damage begins in the centre of the tree's crown and develops outwards, becoming most noticeable in late summer or early autumn. The changed colour of the damaged foliage will persist and the worst affected needles may be shed.

Recognition in the field

The mites are similar in appearance to tiny orange–brown or grey spiders (0.2–0.5 mm) with either six legs (larvae) or eight legs (adults) and can be seen moving over the trees and feeding on the needles (only visible with ×10 lens). They spin a covering of fine silk webbing over the stem and needles, although this is only noticeable when large numbers of mites are present. When mite populations are high, an inspection of the stem during the dormant season (November–April) will reveal many tiny hemispherical orange–brown to reddish eggs on the bark close to the base of the needles, especially in the vicinity of the leading buds.

SECTION 5

Annual life cycle

Overwintering eggs hatch during late April or early May. The mites become active at temperatures of 6–7°C. The larvae take 11–23 days to develop through two stages before becoming adults. Each female lays up to 45 eggs on the stems and occasionally the needles. Successive generations occur throughout the summer resulting in a rapid build-up of numbers during favourable weather conditions. Overwintering eggs are found mainly clustered on the stem near the terminal bud; rarely, if ever, on the needles. In the hot and dry summer of 1991, apparently 'overwintering' eggs were present on trees as early as mid-September. The clear, glass-like remains of egg shells persist on the tree for some time after the larvae have hatched.

Recorded distribution and circumstances where damage occurs

This spider mite is found throughout Britain and Europe on spruces and other conifers. It is also found in most other areas of the world where coniferous trees grow. It is particularly frequent in areas of low rainfall (i.e. less than 1200 mm rain per year) where *Picea abies* is out of its climatic range.

In Christmas tree plantations hot and dry weather favours a rapid increase in *O. ununguis* populations. Damage often occurs in southern and eastern England where conditions best suit the mite, but can occur elsewhere, especially in locations where there is a soil water deficit, i.e. some parts of South Wales and in the West Midlands.

Minimizing damage and control

Avoid growing spruce trees in low rainfall areas and especially on sites that are very hot and dry. Monitor carefully for the presence of overwintering eggs in the spring. [Caution: quite large numbers of eggs seen earlier in autumn do not automatically indicate damage in the next season; losses of these eggs during the winter to natural causes can be high.]

O. ununguis can be controlled successfully by applying a suitable acaricide (e.g. dicofol) in May, or as soon as all the eggs have hatched. At any other time an acaricide that is also active against the eggs will be necessary (e.g. dicofol + tetradifon; clofentezine if it is used before any adult mites are present). [Take note of current Pesticides Regulations – see p. 85.]

Plate 62. Conifer spinning mite damage on Norway spruce.

Plate 63. Needle discoloration caused by conifer spinning mite.

Plate 64. Conifer spinning mite webbing covering a spruce shoot; many mites can be seen on the web.

Plate 66. Overwintering conifer spinning mite eggs on the stem of Norway spruce.

Plate 65. Adult conifer spinning mite.

Conifer spinning mite
Oligonychus ununguis

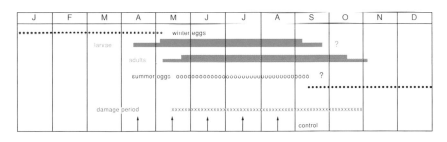

J	F	M	A	M	J	J	A	S	O	N	D
				winter eggs							
		larvae							?		
		adults									
		summer eggs						?			
		damage period	xxxxx						control		

Fig. 25. Conifer spinning mite.

LARGE PINE WEEVIL *(Hylobius abietis)*

Tree species known to be affected

Damage has been recorded on a very wide range of conifers, including all those species used as Christmas trees, as well as broadleaved trees.

Symptoms and consequence of attack

Adult weevils feed on the bark of the stems of young trees, especially just above the root collar. Such feeding can girdle the stem on smaller trees, effectively ring-barking it and causing the death of the tree. Feeding on the side branches of larger trees may cause some slight damage but is unlikely to be a problem on Christmas trees.

Recognition in the field

Adults are typical weevils with a snout and characteristic elbowed antennae. They are 9–13 mm long, black with diffuse transverse yellow markings made up of yellow scales, particularly on the wing cases. Most damage occurs at night, the weevils hiding during the day under bark or in the litter. The larvae are white grubs (up to 15 mm long), slightly curved and wrinkled and with a yellowish brown head.

Annual life cycle

The life cycle from egg to adult varies in length from one to two years in Britain, but in some parts of Europe more than three years may be needed to complete development. The adult weevils can live as long as four years.

Egg-laying takes place in stumps and roots of recently felled conifers, mainly in the spring, although eggs can be found throughout the year. Larvae develop under the bark. Root-feeding larvae are able to move through the soil to another feeding site if their food resource is exhausted. They pupate in a cell constructed in the last feeding place. The peak of adult emergence takes place in the spring.

Recorded distribution and circumstances where damage occurs

Hylobius abietis is found throughout Britain and northern Europe, wherever conifers are grown in woods or plantations. Most damage takes place in spring before egg-laying, or in the autumn before the weevils hibernate in the litter. Damage in a Christmas tree plantation will only be a serious problem where there are managed coniferous woodlands nearby that include areas that have been recently felled. Young transplants are at the greatest risk of damage for up to three years after planting.

Minimizing damage and insect control

Outside of the forest or woodland edge situation damage by *H. abietis* is rarely encountered. Where there is a high risk, or history, of damage being caused, and no other suitable site to grow Christmas trees is available, then obtain transplants that have been dipped in 0.8% permethrin. Where there is a risk of further damage, plants may be treated with an insecticide after planting. At the time of writing several insecticides have either full or off-label approvals for this purpose. Advice should be sought from the suppliers, manufacturers, or the Forestry Commission to ascertain the current approvals. [Take note of current Pesticide Regulations – see p. 85.]

Plate 67. Large pine weevil adults feeding on bark of a pine transplant.

Large pine weevil
Hylobius abietis

J	F	M	A	M	J	J	A	S	O	N	D
			ooooooooooooooooo	eggs				adults – may live up to four years			
larvae (12 – 18 months to complete development)											
						pupae					
	xxxxxxxxxXXXXXXXXXXXXXXXXXXxxxxxxxxxxxxxxxxxxxxxxxxxxxxxxxxxxxxxxxxxXXXXXXXXXXXXXXXXXXxxxxxxx										damage

Fig. 26. Large pine weevil.

SECTION 6

CONTROL OF INSECT PESTS ON CHRISTMAS TREES

It should be stated at the outset of this section that for an insect to become a pest there is likely to be some disturbance factor that has caused an imbalance in the ecosystem enabling certain insects to become more numerous or to be more damaging. Sometimes these factors can be quite obvious to an experienced entomologist, but equally, without prior knowledge of particular circumstances, the cause or factors can be extremely difficult to detect.

TYPES OF CONTROL AVAILABLE

In the recent past, because Christmas tree growing has been widened to use land other than woodland and forests, there has been a strong tendency to follow agricultural practices of intensive management. Such systems commonly demand special attention to pest monitoring or prophylactic applications of insecticides. The latter option always has the possibility of pesticide resistance developing or of leading to an outbreak of another pest.

CULTURAL CONTROL

Norway spruce has been the traditional Christmas tree in Britain, but unfortunately it is not a very good ecological fit on dry sites, particularly on the eastern side of Britain, where soil water deficits lead to stresses in the tree's physiology that allow insects and mites to flourish. If spruce has to be grown in such areas, then Serbian spruce *(Picea omorika)* may be a better option. Similarly certain conifers grow more healthily in their earlier years under some overhead cover; this is particularly so with *Abies grandis* and other true firs, where they not only gain protection from late frosts and bright sunlight but are less prone to the water stresses that enable woolly aphids to become a problem.

It must be remembered when growing non-indigenous tree species that if their native climate is poorly matched with the area to be planted, then the phenology and nutritional vigour of the trees will be upset, leading to susceptibility to pests and diseases. Pruning or shearing to shape trees may have opposite effects to what is expected. For example, removal of dormant terminal buds in pine may lessen the effect of the pine shoot moth, but the resultant dense bushy growth will make effective control of the pine woolly aphid extremely difficult. In another case the pruning and then burning of new unopened adelgid galls in June can help to lessen slight damage where spruce is grown for Christmas trees, whereas the more heavily infested trees are best culled entirely.

NATURAL CONTROL

The choice of tree species or origins used should also take into account any resistance features that are known. Several species of spruce *(Picea)* from Europe and Asia have shown good resistance to green spruce aphid in trials, and future trials with species of true firs *(Abies)* are likely to show differences in susceptibility to other insects. Such choices will minimize chemical control which will have both ecological and financial benefits. The practice of growing Christmas trees in a totally weed-free environment is far removed from what would occur where these conifers regenerate naturally. It is always likely to be the case that tree-feeding insects and mites will flourish in these conditions as there are fewer components to such a habitat, including dead vegetation and the accumulation of fallen needles that would attract over-wintering stages of predators, and fewer flowering plants where the adult stages of both predators and parasites need to feed on nectar and pollen. If natural control is the desired option, then positive management of an adjacent area with flowers in the families *Umbelliferae* and *Compositae* would help to encourage a good range of natural enemies of Christmas tree pests.

BIOLOGICAL CONTROL

When an insect problem is detected on Christmas trees it is worthwhile checking whether any natural enemies are at work before taking any further action. For instance, pine woolly aphid attacks have sometimes attracted natural predatory control that has cut out the need for any further action. Native, natural enemies are likely to be more effective than new introductions because they are better adapted to local conditions such as weather and pest cycles, although there have been notable exceptions. The multicoloured Asian ladybird (*Harmonia axyridis*) introduced to North America in the mid-1980s from Japan has met with some success. However, any initial success of innundative releases of imported natural enemies alone is unlikely to have a long lasting effect in an otherwise sterile Christmas tree plantation due to the missing components in the ecosystem, and releases may have to be repeated every three years or so.

CHEMICAL CONTROL

Substances which are purchased as pesticides are made up of two groups of chemicals: an active ingredient and an inert (or inactive) ingredient. These two in combination make up the pesticide formulation. An active ingredient therefore may be available in more than one type of formulation such as an aerosol, spray, dust, or granule and such formulations are designed to be applied by different systems. It is most important to know what the target is when these are being used. In most cases the pesticide droplet must make contact with the pest in order for it to have an effect. Eggs, tunnelling larvae, or protective layers of wax can make it very difficult for the active ingredient to make contact, so it is essential that the correct formulation and application method are used.

The type of activity that a pesticide has for controlling insects and mites should be considered as well as its persistence in the environment after it has been applied. An ideal pesticide is one that will bring about a significant reduction in damage, and is safe for human usage and non-targeted organisms as well as having short persistence. Systemic insecticides, that are absorbed and then move within the plant and show activity away from the point of entry, are not very effective in slow-growing woody plants and are particularly poor within conifers. For aphids and mites, contact pesticides applied at 'high volume' rates (i.e. over 1000 l/ha) have generally been the most effective when applied to Christmas trees since the spray droplets have to cover and permeate into bud and bark scales where the insects hide. With insects which move relatively little and suck sap (adelgids and aphids) it has been found that the 'ultra low volume' rates (i.e. less than 50 l/ha) have given poor control compared with 'high volume' rates.

Recent developments and trials using soaps and horticultural oils have given very promising results. These chemicals work by acting on waxy coverings of eggs and insects, suffocating and penetrating their tissues. They probably act as repellents by making the plant surface undesirable for settling, feeding, and egg-laying, and have the advantage that they can be used for much of the year under dry conditions provided that the spray strength is adjusted correctly. They have a disadvantage in that glaucous foliage which is sprayed loses its blue cast (which is caused by the natural surface waxes), although subsequent new growth will be blue.

SECTION 6

MONITORING FOR PESTS

Perhaps most important of all to a grower is to walk through the crop periodically and monitor for the arrival or build-up of pest species. It is not unlikely that transplants bought in will come with aphid eggs or overwintering adelgids. These are extremely difficult to see at the dormant stage. Later, tell-tale signs of ants or wasp activity on trees will often lead the observer to the developing pests. It will be best to systematically start monitoring plantations as they enter their second year in the spring. The branches of the trees can be tapped using a stick and a white plastic tray to see what can be dislodged. As insect attack is often clumped it is important to sample every five to ten trees as the row is walked; and to walk down every fourth row at least. Guidance as to when symptoms will be visible in the crop are shown in Figures 27–30. This is one important occasion in growing quality Christmas trees when professional help could be given and may be a better investment than a wrongly applied pesticide application.

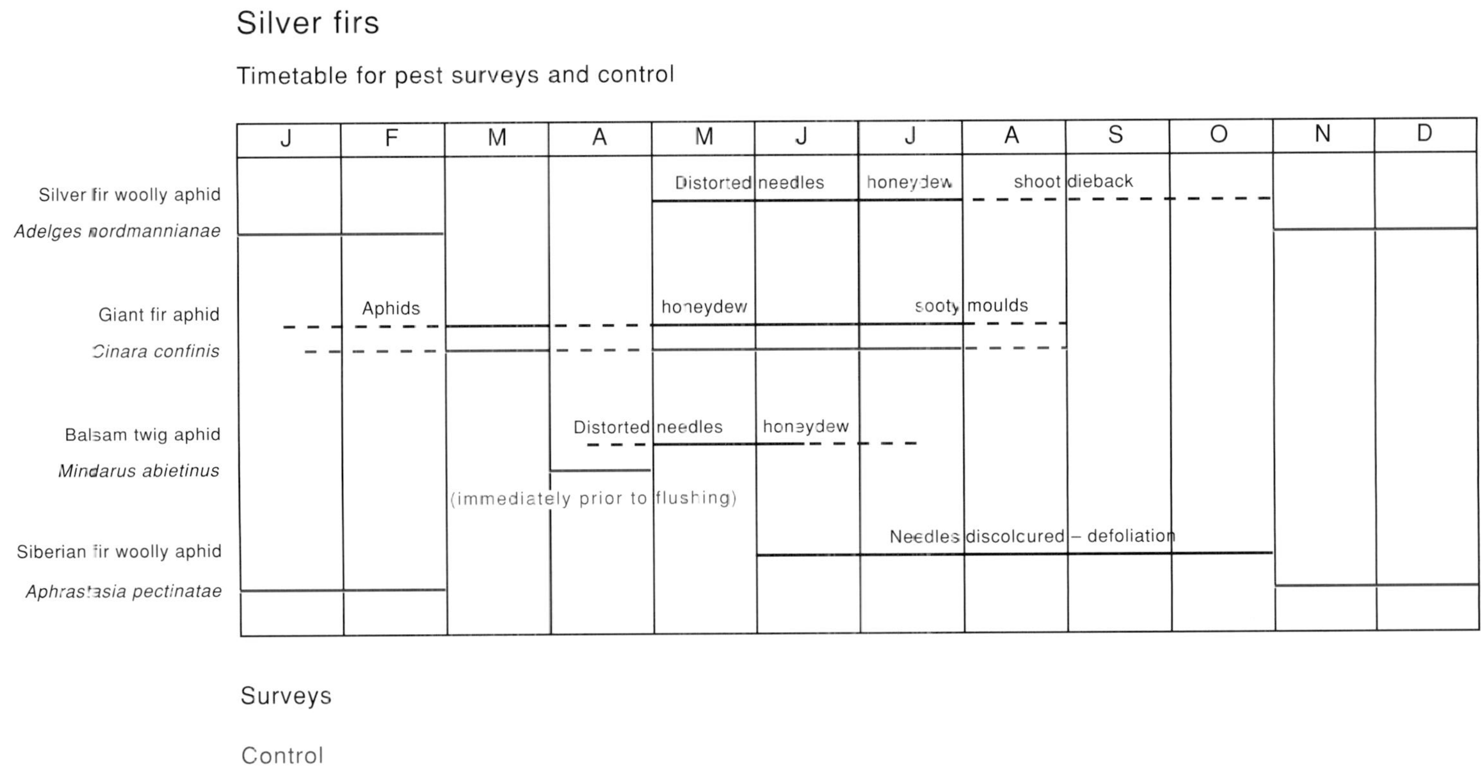

Silver firs

Timetable for pest surveys and control

	J	F	M	A	M	J	J	A	S	O	N	D
Silver fir woolly aphid *Adelges nordmannianae*						Distorted needles	honeydew	shoot dieback				
Giant fir aphid *Cinara confinis*		Aphids			honeydew		sooty moulds					
Balsam twig aphid *Mindarus abietinus*				Distorted needles (immediately prior to flushing)		honeydew						
Siberian fir woolly aphid *Aphrastasia pectinatae*							Needles discoloured – defoliation					

Surveys

Control

Fig. 27. Silver firs: timetable for pest surveys and control.

SECTION 6

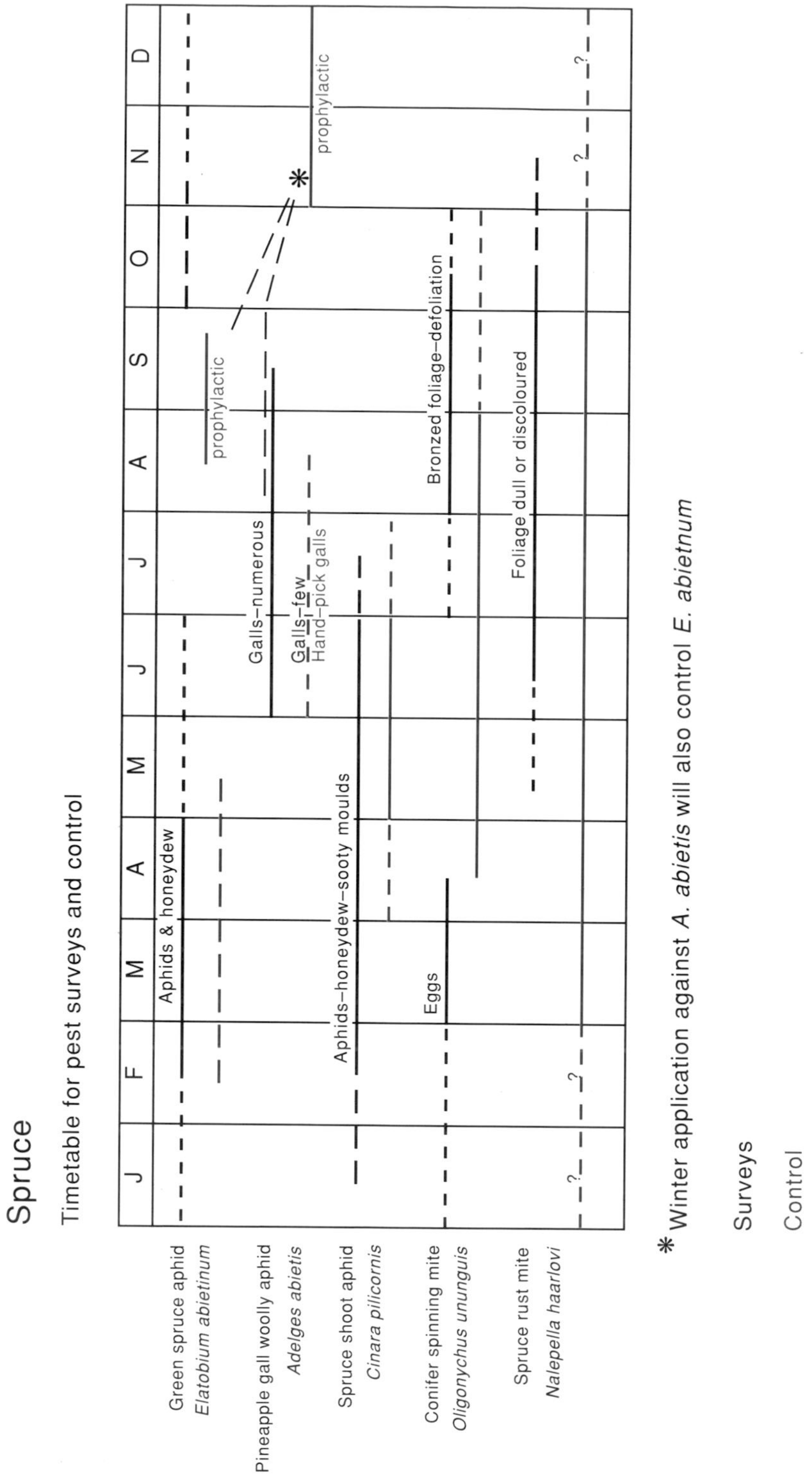

Fig. 28. Spruces: timetable for pest surveys and control.

Pines

Timetable for pest surveys and control

	J	F	M	A	M	J	J	A	S	O	N	D
European pine woolly aphid *Pineus pini*						Wool on new shoots		Yellowing needles				
Grey pine needle aphid *Schizolachnus pineti*				Honeydew			Honeydew+sooty moulds					

Surveys

Control

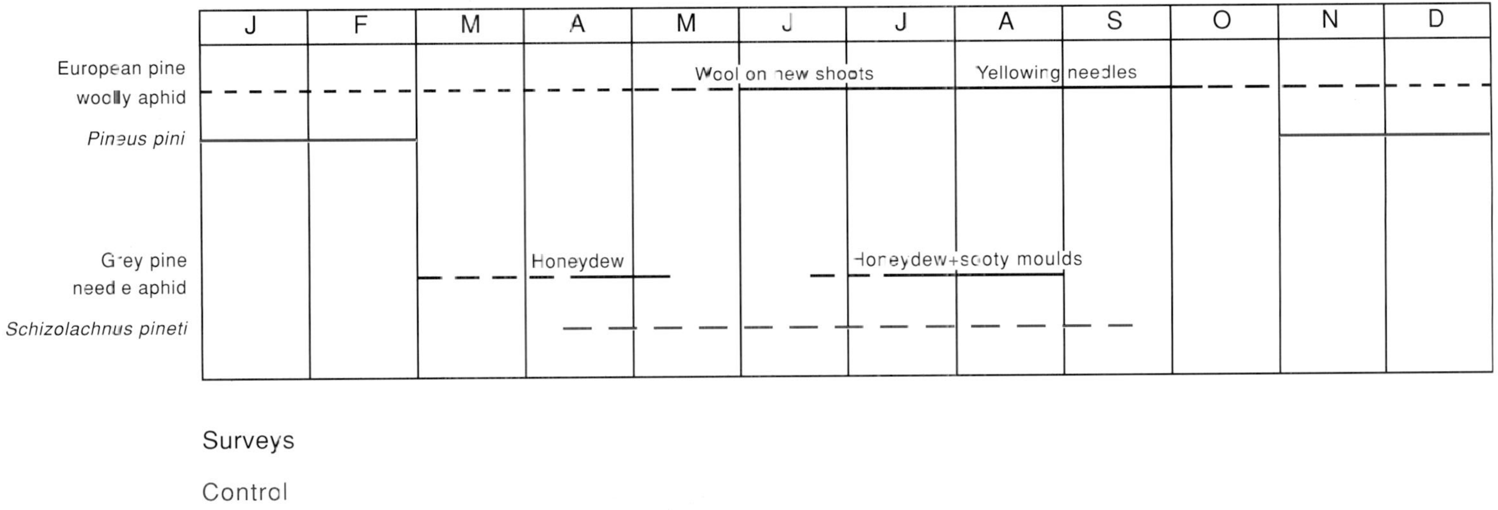

Fig. 29. Pines: timetable for pest surveys and control.

SECTION **6**

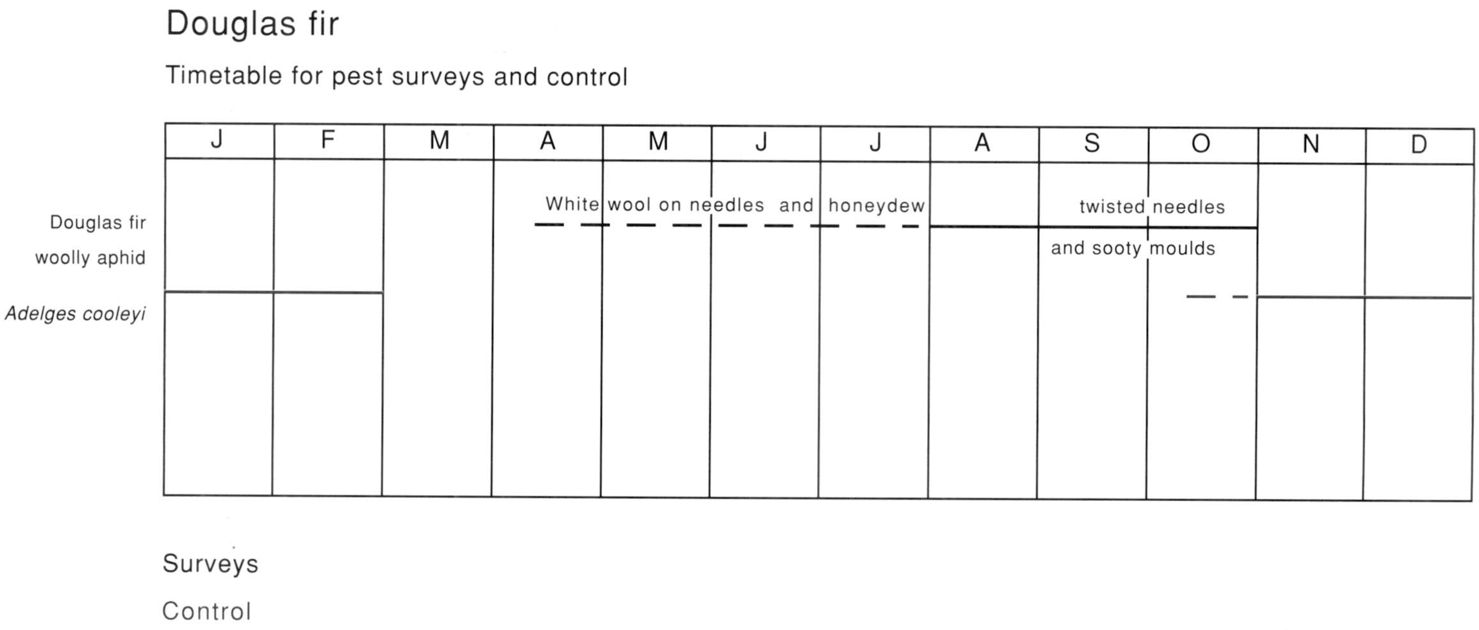

Douglas fir

Timetable for pest surveys and control

	J	F	M	A	M	J	J	A	S	O	N	D
Douglas fir woolly aphid				White wool on needles and honeydew					twisted needles and sooty moulds			
Adelges cooleyi												

Surveys

Control

Fig. 30. Douglas firs: timetable for pest surveys and control.

PESTICIDES REGULATIONS

British law controlling the sale, storage, use, and disposal of 'pesticides' (the definition includes insecticides, fungicides, herbicides, and acaricides) was radically changed and strengthened with the introduction of the Control of Pesticides Regulations 1986 under the Food and Environment Protection Act 1985. The law relating to the use of pesticides on Christmas tree crops is briefly as follows:

1. Before any pesticide can be sold, stored, supplied, used or advertised, it must be Approved (by an appropriate Minister).

2. Most uses to which an 'Approved Product' may be put, the situations in which it may be used, the means by which it may be applied, safety precautions to be observed, and other constraints on its use must be stated on the product label or on any accompanying leaflet. It is illegal to contravene these conditions of use except that:

3. From time to time, Approval is granted for existing Approved products to be used in situations or for purposes not stated on the label – so called 'Off-label' Approvals.

   Such Approvals are usually granted at the request of a grower for a minor use, the demand for which is considered by the manufacturers to be too small to justify the expense of obtaining full Approval.

   Off-label uses are still governed by the safety regulations which apply to full Approvals but the material is used at the user's own risk (i.e. the manufacturer cannot be held responsible for consequent damage to the plant or failure of the treatment).

   Until 31 December 1999 all pesticides with full or provisional label approval for use on any growing crop may be used within forest nurseries, on crops prior to planting out. Christmas trees grown on commercial agricultural and horticultural holdings and in forest nurseries can be regarded as hardy ornamental or forest nursery stock, and are covered by the same arrangements as forest nurseries.

   Anyone who wishes to use a product under the 'Off-label' Approval must first obtain and read a copy of the Notice of Approval, which is available from local Agricultural Departments and Farmers' Union offices.

4. Any user of an Approved professional product who was born later than 31 December 1964 must hold a Certificate of Competence (issued by the National Proficiency Test Council) or be overseen directly by a Certificate Holder.

5. Professional users of pesticides must also comply with the Control of Substances Hazardous to Health Regulations 1988 (COSHH).

FURTHER READING

The most generally useful publication is the UK Pesticide Guide published annually by the British Crop Protection Council and CAB International. This lists Approved professional products (On-label and Off-label) with their active ingredients and approved uses together with general guidance on their safe and effective use and a summary of the relevant legislation. Obtainable from BCPC Publications Sales, Bear Farm, Binfield, Bracknell, Berkshire RG12 5QE.

Approved professional (and amateur) products (but not their recommended uses) are listed in MAFF Reference Book 500, *Pesticides 1997* and subsequent editions published annually by The Stationery Office. This includes a detailed account of the legislation and the Approvals process and also lists pesticides approved for use as wood preservatives and other non-crop purposes. Obtainable from The Stationery Office Publications Centre, PO Box 276, London SW8 5DT.

A summary of the Pesticides Regulations 1986 is given in the free MAFF Leaflet UL79, *Pesticides: guide to the new controls.* Obtainable from MAFF (Publications), Lion House, Willowburn Estate, Alnwick, Northumberland NE66 2PF.

The *Code of Practice for the Safe Use of Pesticides on Farms and Holdings* is obtainable from The Stationery Office. It covers the requirements of both the Control of Pesticides Regulations 1986 and the Control of Substances Harmful to Health Regulations 1988.

GLOSSARY

acaricide	Pesticide used to control mites.
adelgid	Sap-sucking insect in the family Adelgidae (Order Hemiptera). All species feed on conifers and most produce waxy wool. Many species alternate between two different host plants, e.g. *Adelges cooleyi*, *Picea* (the primary host) and *Pseudotsuga* (the secondary host).
aestivate (aestivation)	To pass the summer in a dormant state.
anholocyclic	Reproducing by parthenogenesis throughout the year, without producing sexual forms.
crawler	The newly hatched adelgid that has not settled to feed and has no surface wax secretion.
diapause	Period of suspended development whereby an insect can remain in the same stage for longer than normal.
entomophagous	Feeding mainly on insects.
elybron (elytra)	Hard wing case of a beetle (Family Coleoptera).
eriophyid	Mites in the Superfamily Eriophyoidea (Subclass Acari). Includes the rust mites found free-living on foliage. Typically mites in this group have a sausage to wedge-shaped body about 0.1–0.2 mm long with four legs at the anterior (front) end.
fundatrix	Parthenogenetic female aphid developing from a fertilized egg, or in the case of an adelgid the stage that overwinters on spruce and initiates gall formation the next spring.
gallicolae	Adelgids that develop in galls on the primary host (spruce).
glaucous	Bluish green colour due to covering of a waxy or powdery bloom.
honeydew	Sugary solution excreted by sap sucking insects derived by ingesting plant cell sap (see Plates 37 and 38).
larva(e)	Immature stage of an insect – the types commonly known as caterpillars or grubs.
nymph	Larva or immature stage of an insect (such as a leafhopper, aphid or psyllid) which changes into an adult by developing reproductive organs and wings, rather than by changing into a pupa from which the adult emerges, as do beetles, butterflies and moths.
oviparae	A female aphid (or adelgid) which mates with males and lays fertilized eggs.
ovipositor	Egg-laying structure found at the tip of the abdomen of most female insects.
Palaearctic	Zoogeographical region consisting of Europe, most of Asia north of the Himalayas, and Africa north of the Sahara desert.

parasitoid	An organism alternately parasitic at one stage (e.g. as a larva feeding within another insect) and free-living at another stage (e.g. as fully winged adult).
parthenogenesis (parthenogenetic)	Type of reproduction in which unfertilized females produce viable eggs or young. Common among aphids and closely related groups.
progrediens	The summer generation of an adelgid on the secondary (non-spruce) host plant. This generation usually develops rapidly on the new foliage growth in the spring.
prophylactic	A preventive pesticide, often applied routinely.
saprophyte	An organism that subsists on dead plant material. Some (saprophytic) prefer the term 'saprobe' when referring to fungiand bacteria as these are, strictly speaking, not 'phyta' (plants).
sexupara(e)	A parthenogenetic female aphid which is winged and usually gives birth to both males and oviparae.
sistens	The overwintering generation of an adelgid on the secondary (non-spruce) host plant.
sooty mould	Saprophytic fungus growing on aphid honeydew (see Plate 38).
stomata (stomatal lines)	Small openings with guard cells in the epidermis of green plants; in conifers these are often arranged in parallel lines.
stylet	A set of small bristle-like appendages, being here the modified mouthparts used as a fine tube to inject salvia to enable the withdrawal of sap from plant cells.
sytematics	Methodical system of classification and naming of living organisms.
thorax (thoracic)	Part of an insect's body between the head and the abdomen.
tortrix (tortricid)	Small moth in the Family Tortricidae (Order Lepidoptera).
viviparous (vivipary)	Giving birth to live young.
weevil	Beetle with characteristic elbowed antennae usually borne on a snout (Family Curculionidae, Order Coleoptera).

INDEX OF INSECT AND MITES

SECTION 6

Printed in the United Kingdom for The Stationery Office
C15, 2/98, J0028207, 24503